INDEPENDENT LEARNING PROJECT FOR ADVANCED CHEMISTRY

ILPAC

second edition

PHYSICAL

EQUILIBRIUM I: PRINCIPLES

REVISED BY ANN LAINCHBURY JOHN STEPHENS ALEC THOMPSON

JOHN MURRAY

ACKNOWLEDGEMENTS

We are grateful to CLEAPSS/ASE Laboratory Standards Committee for ensuring that the text meets with current safety recommendations.

Thanks are due to the following examination boards for permission to reproduce questions from past A-level papers: Associated Examining Board: Exercises 28, p. 38 (1974); 40, p. 46 (1976); 51, p. 57 (1979); Part A test 6, p. 24 (1992). Oxford and Cambridge Schools Examination Board: End-of-unit test 1, p. 62 (1990); 7, p. 63 (1990); 11, p. 64 (1991). Southern Universities Joint Board: Exercises 29, p. 40 (1979); 31, p. 40 (1975); 54, p. 61 (1980). University of London Examinations and Assessments Council: Exercises 27, p. 37 (L 1977); 86, p. 75 (N 1975); End-of-unit test 2, p. 62 (L 1979); 3, p. 62 (L 1990); 4, 62 (L 1990); 5, p. 63 (L 1990); 6, p. 63 (L 1990); 8, p. 63 (N 1978); 9, p. 63 (L 1990); 10, p. 64 (L 1991); 12, p. 64 (L 1980); 13, p. 64 (L 1982). University of Oxford Delegacy of Local Examinations: Exercise 48, p. 56 (1979). (The examination boards accept no responsibility whatsoever for the accuracy or method of working in the answers given.)

The photograph on p. 13 reproduced by kind permission of Science Photo Library. All other photographs by the Last Resort Picture Library. The assistance provided by the staff and students of Roding Valley High School, Loughton, Essex and Tuxford School, Tuxford, Newark, Nottinghamshire for the photographs of the experiments is gratefully acknowledged.

Original material produced by the Independent Learning Project for Advanced Chemistry sponsored by the Inner London Education Authority

First edition published 1983
by John Murray (Publishers) Ltd
50 Albemarle Street
London W1X 4BD

Second edition 1995, 1999

Reprinted 2002 (twice)

British Library Cataloguing in Publication Data
A catalogue record for this book is available from the British Library

ISBN 0-7195-5336-9

Design and layouts by John Townson/Creation
Illustrations by Barking Dog Art

Produced by Gray Publishing
Typeset in 10/12 pt Times and Helvetica

Printed in Great Britain by Selwood Printing Ltd. West Sussex

CONTENTS

EQUILIBRIUM I: PRINCIPLES

Symbols used in ILPAC

Computer program

Discussion

Experiment

Model-making

Reading

Revealing Exercise

Video programme

A- level question

A-level part question

A-level question; Special Paper

A-level supplementary question

International hazard symbols

Corrosive

Explosive

Harmful or irritant

Highly flammable

Oxidising

Radioactive

Toxic

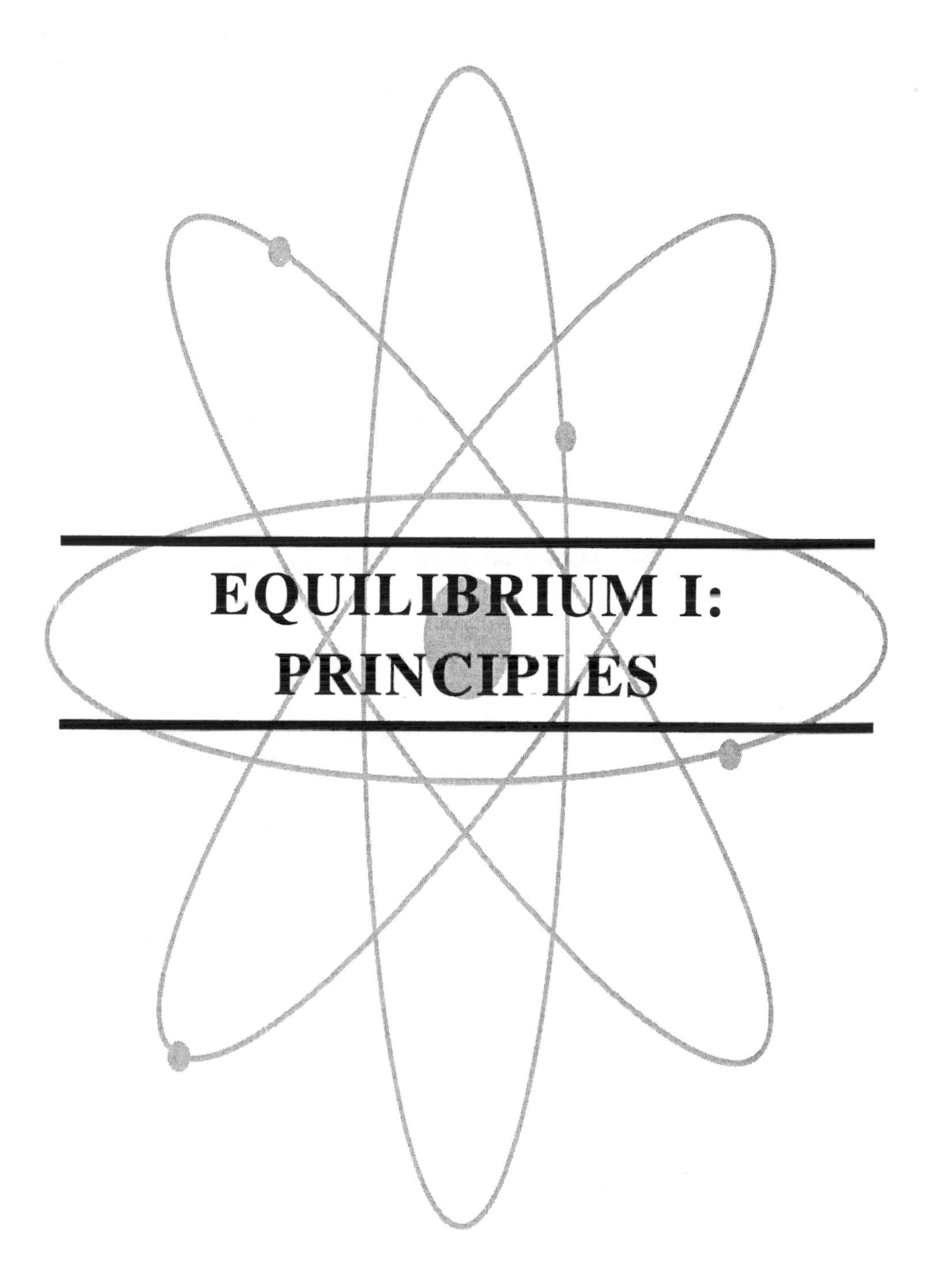

EQUILIBRIUM I: PRINCIPLES

INTRODUCTION

This is the first of two volumes on the subject of equilibrium (the other is ILPAC Volume 7), which is an important concept in every branch of chemistry. In this volume we outline the principles of equilibrium and show that they are applicable to a wide variety of situations.

In Part A we deal with the qualitative aspects of equilibrium and show you how to apply a useful rule, known as Le Chatelier's principle, to summarise the way equilibrium systems react to changes in conditions.

In Part B we introduce the equilibrium law, a mathematical statement which describes all equilibrium systems. We show you how to apply the equilibrium law to a number of different systems, including the equilibrium between a slightly soluble salt and its saturated solution, and the distribution of a solute between two different solvents. Further applications appear in ILPAC Volume 7.

There are five experiments in this volume, four of them in Part B.

There is an ILPAC video programme; however, it is not essential but you should try to see it at the appropriate time if it is available.

Pre-knowledge

Before you start work on this book you should be able to:

- State some examples of reversible reactions.
- Write a thermochemical equation for a reaction, given the appropriate data.
- Write simple definitions of the following terms:
  - **a** amount of substance,
  - **b** molar mass,
  - **c** concentration,
  - **d** solubility,
  - **e** partial pressure,
  - **f** catalyst.
- Write equations, including state symbols, for the reactions between
  - **a** ethanol and ethanoic acid,
  - **b** iron and steam,
  - **c** calcium chloride and sodium carbonate.
- Rearrange an equation of the type

$$5 = \frac{3x}{(1-x)(3-2x)}$$

into a standard quadratic equation of the form $ax^2 + bx + c = 0$.

QUALITATIVE ASPECTS OF EQUILIBRIUM

EQUILIBRIUM SYSTEMS

OBJECTIVES When you have finished this chapter you should be able to:
- recognise that **reversible changes** are an essential feature of equilibrium systems;
- quote examples of different **types of equilibrium system;**
- use the term **phase** to distinguish between **homogeneous** and **heterogeneous systems.**

1.1 Reversible reactions

Most of the chemistry you have studied so far has been concerned with reactions which appcar to 'go to completion'. For example, when magnesium burns in oxygen, **all** of the metal is converted to magnesium oxide, and when a lump of calcium carbonate is dropped into an excess of hydrochloric acid, **all** of the solid reacts

$$2Mg\ (s\ ) + O_2\ (g) \rightarrow 2MgO\ (s)$$

$$CaCO_3\ (s) + 2HCl\ (aq) \rightarrow CaCl_2\ (aq) + H_2O\ (l) + CO_2\ (g)$$

In neither of these cases is there any indication that the reverse change occurs.

The idea of **reversible** change is very familiar in systems where no chemical reaction occurs; for example, ice melting to water and water freezing to ice. However, you have also met some **reversible reactions**, i.e. chemical reactions which can be made to 'go both ways'.

For example, if iron is heated in a current of steam, it can be converted completely to iron(II) diiron(III) oxide, Fe_3O_4

$$3Fe\ (s) + 4H_2O\ (g) \rightarrow Fe_3O_4\ (s) + 4H_2\ (g)$$

But if the oxide is heated in a current of hydrogen the reverse reaction occurs

$$Fe_3O_4\ (s) + 4H_2\ (g) \rightarrow 3Fe\ (s) + 4H_2O\ (g)$$

Pre-test

To find out whether you are ready to start Part A try the following test, which is based on the pre-knowledge items. You should not spend more than 30 minutes on this test. Hand your answers to your teacher for marking.

1. Write a thermochemical equation summarising the information given in the energy level diagram below:

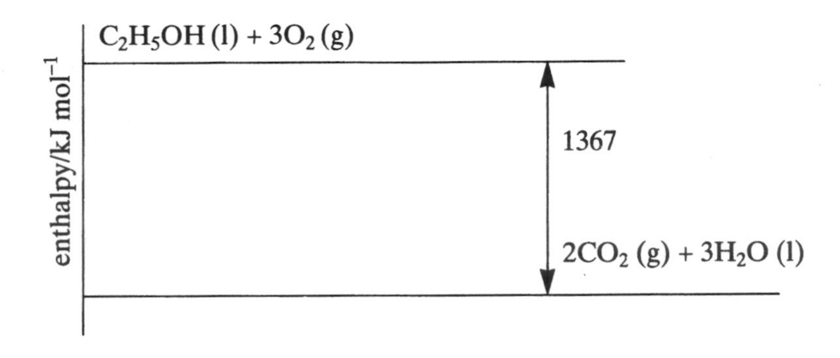

(2)

2. What effect does a catalyst have on a chemical reaction? (1)

3. Define the following terms, stating the usual units:
   a concentration, (2)
   b molar mass, (2)
   c solubility, (2)
   d partial pressure. (2)

4. Write equations, including state symbols, for the reactions between:
   a ethanol and ethanoic acid, (2)
   b iron and steam, (2)
   c calcium chloride and sodium carbonate. (2)

5. Rearrange into standard quadratic form the equation:

$$4 = \frac{6x}{(1-2x)(2-x)}$$

(3)

(Total: 20 marks)

However, if the system is closed (no material can pass in or out) so that reactants and products are always in contact, both reactions can occur at the same time. Then the system achieves a state of equilibrium in which the reversible changes 'cancel each other out'.

We can represent this state of equilibrium by a 'double-ended arrow', $\rightleftharpoons$. (In some books you may find the 'equals' sign, =, used for this purpose.) We use this symbol to imply that two opposing processes are occurring at the same time, for example

$$3Fe\ (s) + 4H_2O\ (g) \rightleftharpoons Fe_3O_4\ (s) + 4H_2\ (g)$$

Does it make any difference if we write the equation the other way round?

$$Fe_3O_4\ (s) + 4H_2\ (g) \rightleftharpoons 3Fe\ (s) + 4H_2O\ (g)$$

We will answer this question shortly.

Other examples of equilibrium systems you may have studied in your pre-A-level courses are

$$N_2\ (g) + 3H_2\ (g) \rightleftharpoons 2NH_3\ (g)$$

$$CaCO_3\ (s) + CO_2\ (g) + H_2O\ (l) \rightleftharpoons Ca(HCO_3)_2\ (aq)$$

You may be surprised to learn that it is useful to consider **all** chemical reactions as equilibrium systems, even when the processes cannot be readily reversed. We consider different types of equilibrium system in the next section.

1.2 Types of equilibrium system

There are many situations in which opposing changes occur at the same time, leading to a state of equilibrium. The different types of equilibrium we shall discuss in ILPAC can be classified as shown in Table 1.

Table 1

Physical processes

1. Pure solid/pure liquid.
2. Pure liquid/pure vapour.
3. Pure solid/pure vapour.
4. Pure solid in contact with a solution, dissolving and crystallising occurring together.
5. Solute distributed (or partitioned) between two solvents which are immiscible (i.e. do not mix – like oil and water).

Chemical processes

6. Chemical equilibria with reactants and products in the same phase.*
7. Chemical equilibria with reactants and products in different phases. Types 6 and 7 cover all chemical processes, but they may be further subdivided:
8. A slightly soluble ionic solid
9. Acid–base systems (dealt with more fully in the ILPAC Volume 7: Acids and Bases)
10. Redox systems (dealt with more fully in the ILPAC Volume 7: Redox Reactions)
11. Complex ion formation (dealt with more fully in the ILPAC Volume 11: Transition Elements).

*We explain the term 'phase' in the next section.

1.3 Phase

A phase is defined as any uniform (i.e. homogeneous) part of a system which is different from the rest of the system and separated from it by a distinct boundary. Any sample of that phase has exactly the same properties and chemical composition. Here are some examples.

Figure 1

Figure 2

Figure 3

Figure 4

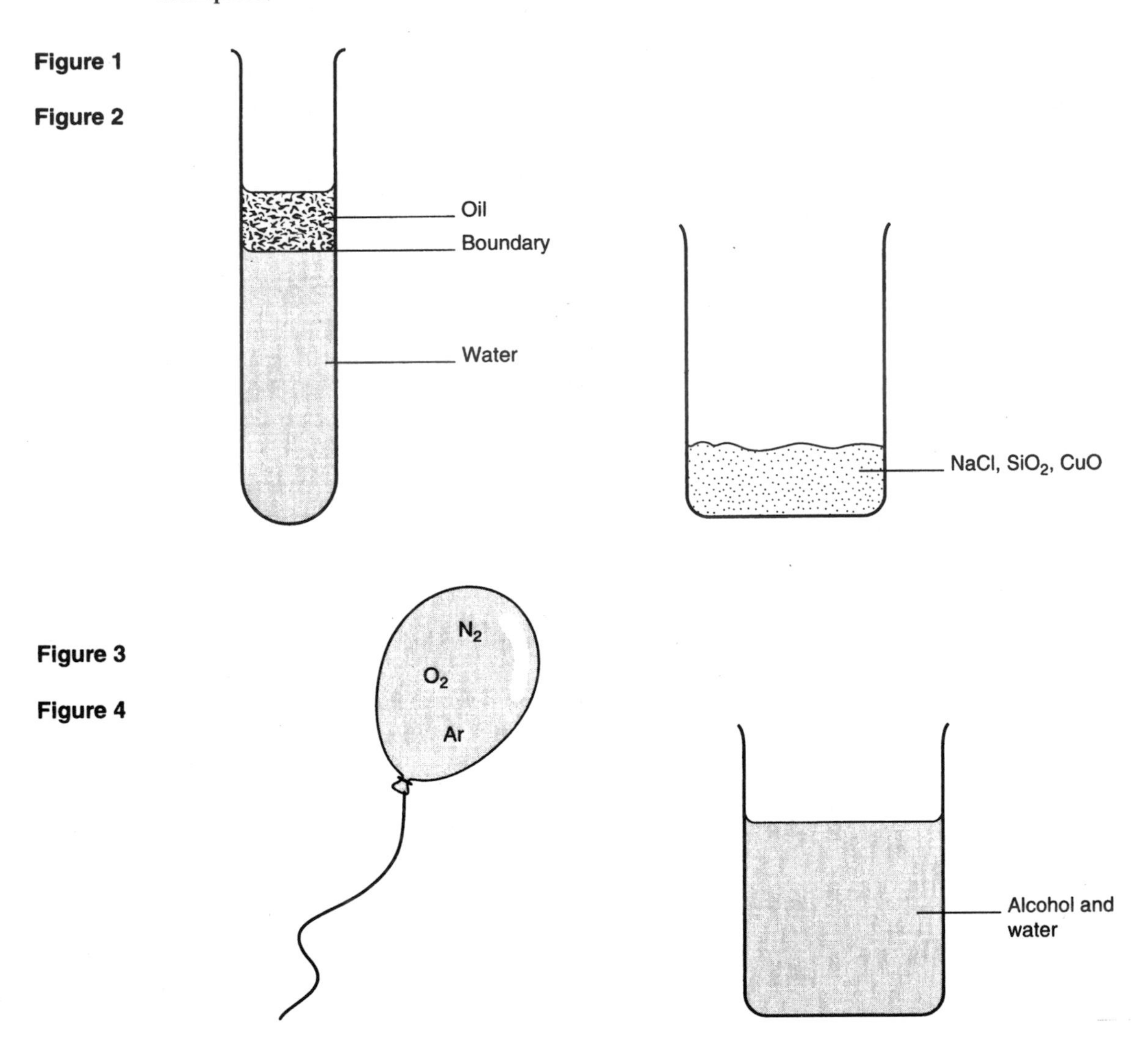

1. The contents of a tube containing oil and water is a system with two phases (Fig. 1).
2. A mixture of salt, sand and copper(II) oxide, even when finely ground, is a three-phase system (Fig. 2).
3. There can be only one gas phase because gases always diffuse into one another to form a homogeneous mixture. Air is a one-phase system (Fig. 3).
4. Miscible liquids form a one-phase system, because, like gases, they form a homogeneous mixture. An example is alcohol and water (Fig. 4).

Some of these different types of equilibrium system are illustrated in Fig. 5. It will be useful for you later on if you can identify the various types. So now do Exercise 1.

EXERCISE 1
Answers on page 76

Look at the list of different types of equilibrium system in Table 1. For each type, choose one suitable example from those illustrated in Fig. 5.

1.4 Some examples of equilibrium systems

Figure 5

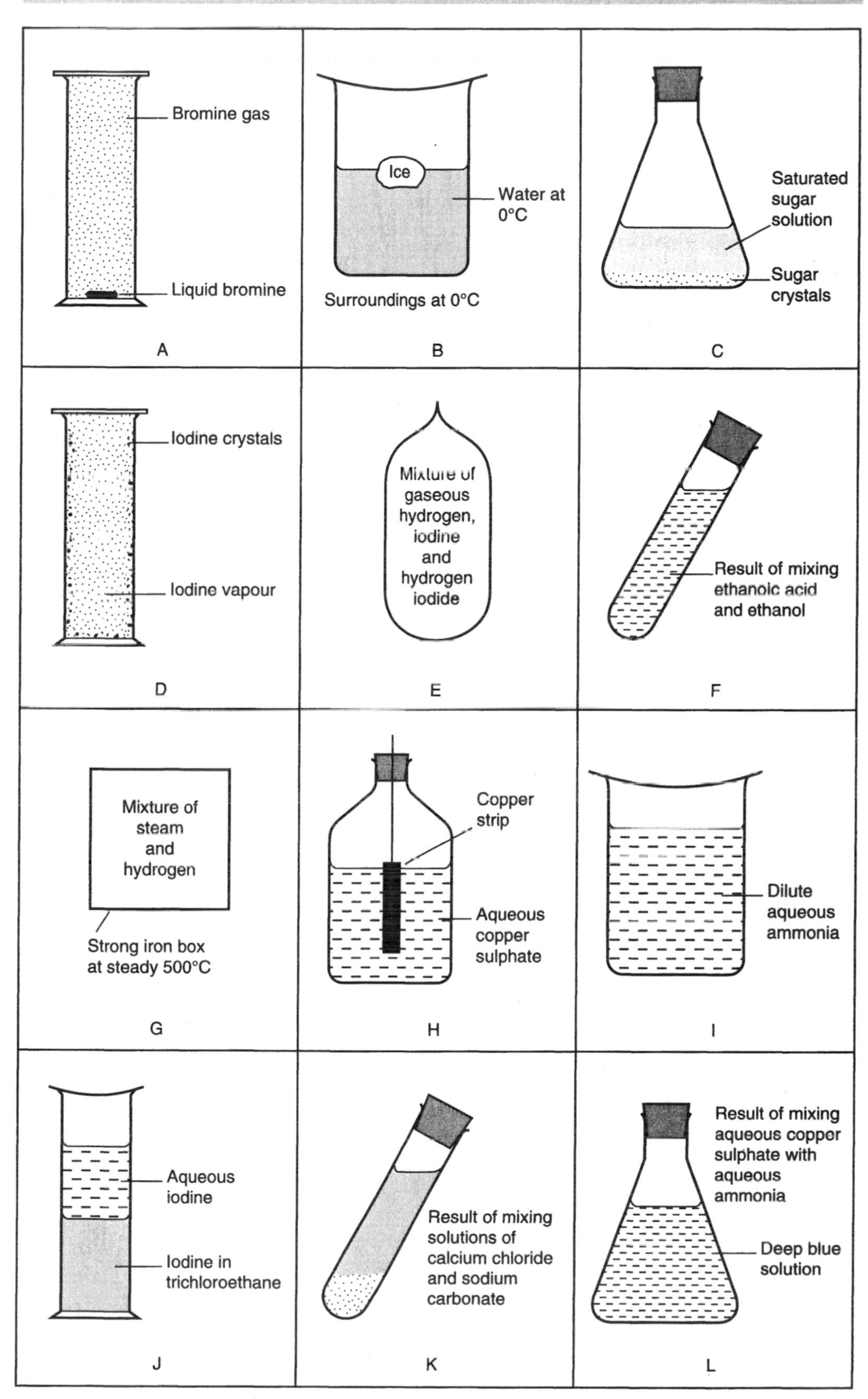

1.5 Equilibria in homogeneous and heterogeneous systems

Another way of classifying different equilibrium systems divides them into two types: homogeneous and heterogeneous systems.

A homogeneous system consists of one phase only.
A heterogeneous system consists of more than one phase.

EXERCISE 2
Answers on page 76

Look again at the equilibrium systems illustrated in Fig. 5 and decide whether they are homogeneous or heterogeneous. Ignore the 'air space' inside the containers and note that only in G is the container part of the equilibrium system.

If you can identify a heterogeneous system, solving numerical problems will be easier, because you can simplify the arithmetic by certain assumptions. Of course, you can easily identify a heterogeneous system from the chemical equation, provided state symbols are included.

1.6 General statements about equilibrium

Different types of equilibrium system are often dealt with in books under separate headings or even in separate chapters. In ILPAC we want to emphasise that the principles which apply to any one equilibrium system apply to all; we can make two general statements which apply throughout.

1. All equilibrium systems share the same general characteristics.
2. All equilibrium systems can be described quantitatively by the equilibrium law.

We deal with the equilibrium law in Part B. The next chapter will enable you to learn what the characteristics of equilibrium are.

THE EQUILIBRIUM STATE

It can be demonstrated that **all** equilibrium systems share the same characteristics. However, we will merely illustrate these characteristics by reference to a few simple examples.

OBJECTIVES

When you have finished this chapter you should be able to:

- list, in your own words, four **characteristics of the equilibrium state;**
- illustrate and explain each characteristic by reference to a particular equilibrium system.

2.1 Characteristics of the equilibrium state

Read about the characteristics of the equilibrium state in your textbook(s). Make sure that you understand the difference between macroscopic properties (bulk properties) and molecular properties. If you are unable to watch the video referred to below, look for a detailed account of an experiment which demonstrates that equilibrium is dynamic.

If it is available, watch the first part of the ILPAC video programme 'Equilibrium', in which we demonstrate by experiment that an equilibrium system is dynamic.

Use the notes you have written to help you with the next exercise.

EXERCISE
Teacher-marked

Write an account of an experiment which shows conclusively that equilibrium is dynamic.

The following exercise tests your understanding of the characteristics of dynamic equilibrium.

EXERCISE 3
Answers on page 76

Make a copy of Table 2 (from page 10) to fill a whole page.

a For each equilibrium system in Fig. 5 write, in the second column of Table 2, an equation which identifies the opposing changes which are occurring at equal rates. Two examples are given.

Note that since the changes are reversible, it is just as correct to write the equations the other way round.

In some cases, there may be more than one equilibrium in the same system; e.g. in all those involving aqueous solutions, the equilibrium

$$H_2O\ (l) \rightleftharpoons H_2O\ (g)$$

is involved as well as the more important one required in this exercise. If you cannot decide which is the 'important' equilibrium, then write down more than one equation, as in Fig. 5(I).

b In the third column of your copy of Table 2, for each system write down at least three observable properties, other than temperature, which have constant values despite the continuous change on the atomic scale.

Table 2

System	Equation	Constant macroscopic properties
A	Br_2 (l) ⇌ Br_2 (g)	Volume of liquid bromine Mass of bromine gas Colour of gas
B		
C		
D		
E		
F	CH_3CO_2H (l) + C_2H_5OH (l) ⇌ $CH_3CO_2C_2H_5$ (l) + H_2O (l)	Mass of ethanol Amount of water Volume of liquid phase
G		
H		
I		
J		
K		
L		

2.2 Why equilibrium systems are 'closed'

All the systems shown in Fig. 5 are closed, and you have learned that equilibrium can only be reached in a closed system. In the next exercise you decide just how necessary it is for an equilibrium system to be closed.

EXERCISE 4
Answers on page 77

Look again at Fig. 5.

a What would happen in systems A, D, E and G if the system were made 'open' by removing the cover or drilling a hole in the container? Why would equilibrium not be maintained?

b In practice, it is not always so important to have a closed system as it is in the examples discussed in **a**. Look, for example, at system K and explain why it is not very important that the tube should be stoppered.

2.3 How equilibrium systems are established

Once a system is at equilibrium, it is impossible to determine whether the system was prepared by starting with reactants or products. In Fig. 5, for example, you could not tell whether system E was prepared by starting with a mixture of hydrogen and iodine or by heating hydrogen iodide. To see if you can work out how equilibrium might be established, try the next exercise.

EXERCISE 5
Answers on page 77

Choose any three systems, except E, from Fig. 5 and state alternative practical ways of setting up each one from different starting points. (Hint: A–G, and J, should be easy; the rest are perhaps not quite so straightforward – try at least one of these also.)

It can sometimes take quite a long time for a system to reach equilibrium from a given starting point. For example, mixtures of ethyl ethanoate and water need about three days to reach equilibrium at room temperature, even when a catalyst is present.

Therefore you should do Experiment 2(a) (page 29) as soon as it is convenient, so that the mixtures you prepare will be ready for examination in Experiment 2(b) in a few days time.

In the next chapter you study the ways in which equilibrium, once established, can be disturbed.

FACTORS AFFECTING THE POSITION OF EQUILIBRIUM

A system in chemical equilibrium is defined by an equation, as you have seen in Exercise 3. However, one system can have many different states, and change between one state and another can be brought about in various ways.

OBJECTIVES

When you have finished this chapter you should be able to:
- explain what is meant by the term **position of equilibrium;**
- list the **factors which affect equilibria;**
- state **Le Chatelier's principle.**

3.1 Position of equilibrium

We often use the term 'position of equilibrium' to refer to one particular state of an equilibrium system. One state, or position, differs from another in the concentrations of the substances present in the equilibrium mixture.

When the conditions change so that the system is no longer in equilibrium, the two opposing reactions no longer cancel each other out. The concentrations of all the substances change until a new position of equilibrium is established.

For example, if a change in conditions in the system

$$H_2\ (g) + I_2\ (g) \rightleftharpoons 2HI\ (g)$$

results in the reaction from the left to right becoming faster than the reverse reaction, more HI will be formed until the rates of forward and backward reaction are equal again and a new position of equilibrium is established. In this case, we can say that:

'the equilibrium has shifted towards more products',

or

'the position of equilibrium has shifted to the right'.

You should note that references to 'right' and 'left', or to 'reactants' and 'products' in equilibrium systems, are quite useless unless an equation is written down, because, of course, the equation can be written either way round.

You are already familiar with the factors which affect the **rates** of chemical reactions from your pre-A-level work. These are listed below.

1. Concentration.
2. Temperature.
3. Pressure.
4. Catalysts.

A system at equilibrium appears to consist of two reactions: a forward reaction and its reverse. It seems reasonable to assume, therefore, that the factors which affect rates might also affect equilibrium systems.

You will study the effect of each of these factors on different equilibrium systems. In your study you will make use of a very important principle, which can be applied to **all** changes in equilibrium position.

3.2 Le Chatelier's principle

Henri Le Chatelier, a French chemist, investigated changes in equilibrium systems many years ago. His work, published in 1895, gives us a useful 'rule of thumb' to predict the direction in which the position of equilibrium will shift under varying conditions of concentration, temperature, pressure and with or without the presence of a catalyst.

A literal translation from the French of Le Chatelier's own formulation of the principle follows. You should look for a simpler wording in your textbook(s) for the next exercise!

Henri Louis Le Chatelier (1850–1936). Pictured here as a student of the Ecole Polytechnique in France.

'Every system in chemical equilibrium submitted to the influence of an exterior force which tends to cause variation either in its temperature or its condensation (pressure, concentration, number of molecules in unit volume) in its totality or only in some one of its parts can undergo only those interior modifications which, if they occurred alone, would produce a change of temperature, or of condensation, of a sign contrary to that resulting from the exterior force.'

EXERCISE 6
Answer on page 78

Write, in your own words, a simple statement of Le Chatelier's principle.

The value of Le Chatelier's principle should become clearer to you when you apply it to specific equilibrium systems in the following sections. Remember that the principle allows you to predict the **direction** of any change in equilibrium position but not the **extent** of the change.

■ 3.3 The effect on equilibrium of changing concentrations

OBJECTIVE

When you have finished this section you should be able to:

- use Le Chatelier's principle to predict the effect on equilibrium systems of **changing concentrations.**

We start this section with a simple experiment. You can consolidate your understanding of the results by reading (after the experiment) and by applying them to other systems.

In the experiment we introduce a convenient and widely used piece of shorthand. Square brackets enclosing the formula of a substance mean 'concentration of', for example [Fe^{3+} (aq)] means 'the concentration of aqueous iron(III) ions'.

EXPERIMENT 1 The effect of concentration changes on equilibria

Aim The purpose of this experiment is to find out how a system in equilibrium responds to a change in concentration of components in the mixture.

Introduction Iron(III) ions and thiocyanate ions react in solution to produce thiocyanatoiron(III), a complex ion, according to the equation:

$$Fe^{3+}(aq) + SCN^-(aq) \rightleftharpoons Fe(SCN)^{2+}(aq)$$

pale yellow — colourless — blood-red

The colour produced by the complex ion can indicate the position of equilibrium. (The colour of the Fe^{3+} (aq) ion is in fact a very pale violet, but solutions of iron(III) salts are usually yellow, due to the formation of other complexes.)

Requirements

- safety spectacles
- 4 test-tubes and test-tube rack
- 2 teat-pipettes
- distilled water
- potassium thiocyanate solution, 0.5 M KSCN
- iron(III) chloride solution, 0.5 M $FeCl_3$
- ammonium chloride, NH_4Cl (**warning**: harmful by ingestion, wash hands after use)
- spatula
- glass stirring rod

Procedure

1. Mix together one drop of 0.5 M iron(III) chloride solution and one drop of 0.5 M potassium thiocyanate solution in a test-tube and add about 5 cm^3 of distilled water to form a pale orange–brown solution.
2. Divide this solution into four equal parts in four test-tubes.
3. Add one drop of 0.5 M iron(III) chloride to one test-tube. Add one drop of 0.5 M potassium thiocyanate to a second.
4. Compare the colours of these solutions with the untouched samples. Enter your observations in a copy of Results Table 1.

5. Add a spatula-ful of solid ammonium chloride to a third test-tube and stir well. Compare the colour of this solution with the remaining tube and note your observation.

   Ammonium chloride removes iron(III) ions from the equilibrium by forming complex ions such as $FeCl_4^-$. A possible reaction is:

$$Fe^{3+}\,(aq) + 4Cl^-\,(aq) \rightleftharpoons FeCl_4^-\,(aq)$$

   The effect is to reduce the concentration of iron(III) ions.

Before you leave the laboratory, shake the tubes you prepared for Experiment 2.

Interpretation of results

Having made three observations, suggest a **cause** for each colour change (in terms of the concentrations of the coloured species) and then suggest what can be **inferred** about a shift in the position of equilibrium.

If a pattern has emerged, then you can make a prediction based on the results of the experiment.

Results Table 1

Change	Observation	Cause	Inference
$[Fe^{3+}]$ increased			
$[SCN^-]$ increased			
$[Fe^{3+}]$ decreased			

(Specimen results on page 78.)

Questions

Answers on page 78

1. How would the position of equilibrium be affected by increasing the concentration of $FeSCN^{2+}$?
2. For each imposed change show how the shift in equilibrium position conforms to Le Chatelier's principle.

To consolidate the work done in Experiment 1, read about the effect of **concentration changes** on equilibrium. Look for the application of Le Chatelier's principle to the direction of change in equilibrium position, but leave until later any references to the extent of change and the equilibrium law. This will help you with the Revealing Exercise which follows.

EXERCISE

Revealing

Consider the following equilibrium system:

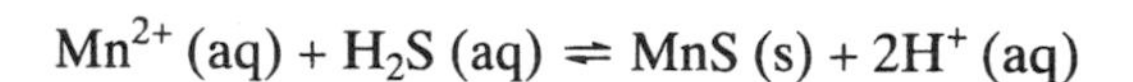

$$Mn^{2+}\,(aq) + H_2S\,(aq) \rightleftharpoons MnS\,(s) + 2H^+\,(aq)$$

Q1 What effect does the addition of more H_2S have on the position of equilibrium? (Assume the system is not saturated with H_2S already.)

A1 The position of equilibrium shifts to the right.

Q2 Explain your answer to question 1 using Le Chatelier's principle.

A2 The change imposed on the system is an increase in the concentration of H_2S. The position of equilibrium will shift to use up some of the added H_2S. In doing so, more MnS (s) and H^+ (aq) will be formed.

Q3 What effect does passing hydrogen chloride gas into the mixture have on the position of equilibrium?

A3 The equilibrium shifts to the left.

Q4 Explain your answer to question 3 using Le Chatelier's principle.

A4 Hydrogen chloride gas dissolves to produce hydrogen ions in solution, thus increasing their concentration. The system responds by shifting to the left to reduce the concentration by producing more Mn^{2+} (aq) and H_2S (aq).

Q5 What effect does the addition of alkali have on the position of equilibrium?

A5 The equilibrium shifts to the right.

Q6 Explain your answer to question 5 using Le Chatelier's principle.

A6 The alkali reduces the concentration of hydrogen ions by neutralisation; therefore the forward reaction occurs to increase it again.

Both of the equilibrium systems we have used to study the effect of concentration changes are homogeneous systems. The situation is usually simpler in heterogeneous systems, as we now show.

3.4 Pure solids and pure liquids in equilibrium systems

One of the equilibrium systems you have already studied is shown again in Fig. 6. This is a heterogeneous system containing a pure solid. What is the effect on the equilibrium position of adding more solid sugar?

Figure 6

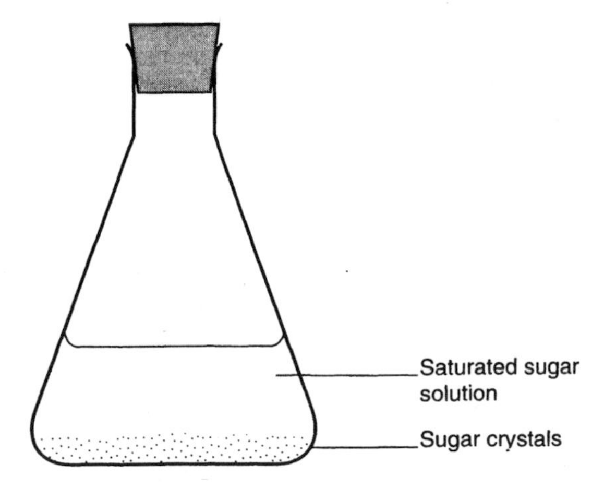

Clearly the concentration of sugar in the solution cannot increase because it is already saturated. If it takes five lumps of sugar to saturate the solution in a cup of tea, six lumps will not make it any sweeter! So the equilibrium position remains unchanged. How does this tie in with Le Chatelier's principle?

To answer this question you must consider what we mean by 'the concentration of a solid'. In a solution, and in a gas, the concentration changes as the particles (molecules, atoms or ions) become closer together or further apart. In a solid the particles are in fixed positions relative to each other; this means that the concentration is also fixed. In effect, the concentration of a solid is equivalent to its **density**.

Therefore, by adding more sugar to the system in Fig. 6, we change the **amount** of solid present but not its **concentration**. Since an equilibrium state, or position, is specified by the concentrations of substances present, it follows that adding more solid sugar does not affect the equilibrium position.

You can apply a very similar argument to pure liquids in equilibrium systems; try this in the next exercise. You may find it useful to refer to your textbooks.

EXERCISE 7

Answers on page 78

Figure 7 shows another of the equilibrium systems you have already considered.

Figure 7

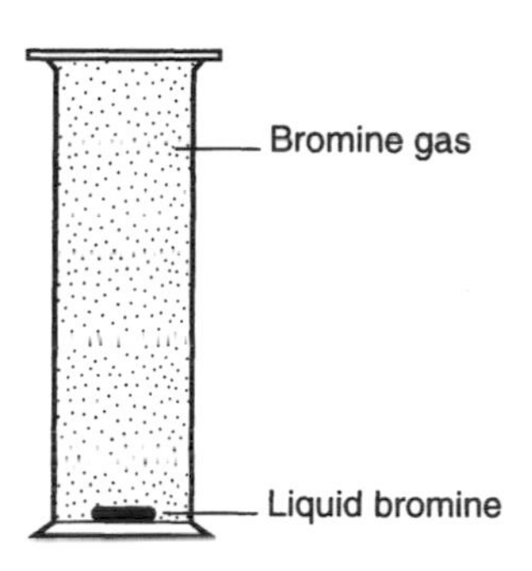

Explain why the addition of more liquid does not change the concentration of bromine gas.

Try one more exercise to make sure you have grasped this idea.

EXERCISE 8

Answers on page 78

Figure 8 shows a copper strip in equilibrium with a solution of copper(II) ions. What would happen to the system if the copper strip were replaced by a fine copper wire? Explain.

Figure 8

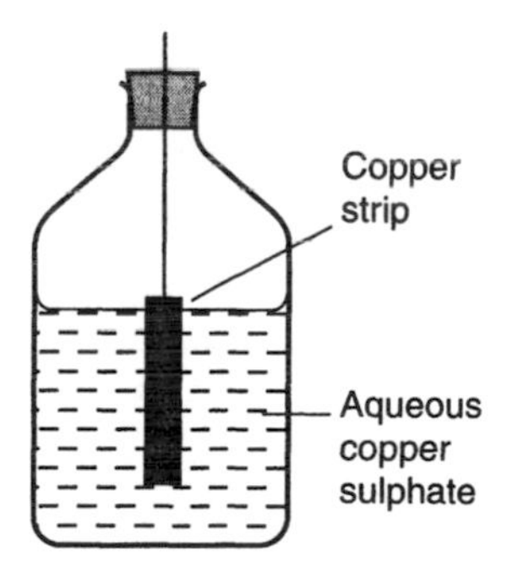

Remember that although we have only discussed a few examples, the general rules apply to all equilibrium systems.

The concentration of a pure solid, or a pure liquid, is constant.

Changing the amount of pure solid, or pure liquid, in an equilibrium mixture does not disturb the equilibrium.

Now we consider the effect of temperature changes.

3.5 The effect on equilibrium of changing temperature

OBJECTIVE When you have finished this section you should be able to:
- apply Le Chatelier's principle to the effect on equilibrium of **changing temperature.**

For simplicity we start by considering the effect of temperature change on a physical process, but you can apply the principle to all equilibria, both physical and chemical. Consider again the system shown in Fig. 9

$$Br_2\,(l) \rightleftharpoons Br_2\,(g)$$

Figure 9

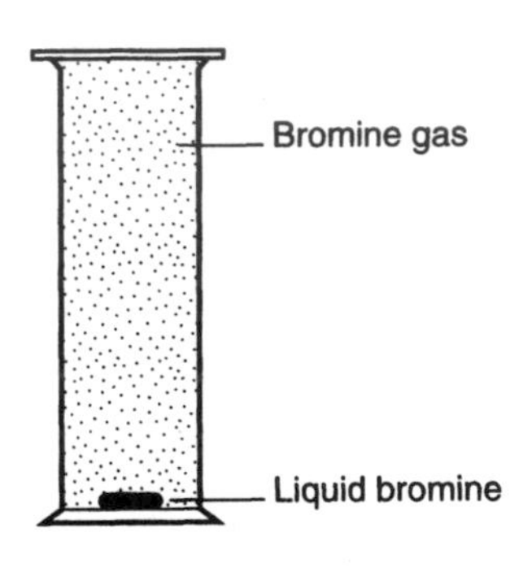

Common experience (usually of open systems) tells you that if a liquid is warmed, it vaporises. If this system is heated, more gaseous bromine is formed.

To help you apply Le Chatelier's principle to this system, and to generalise the effect of temperature on other equilibrium systems, work through the following Revealing Exercise.

EXERCISE
Revealing

Q1 Using your data book, write a thermochemical equation for the vaporisation of bromine, and draw an energy level diagram.

A1 $Br_2\,(l) \rightleftharpoons Br_2\,(g)$; $\Delta H^{\ominus}(331\ K) = +15.0\ kJ\ mol^{-1}$

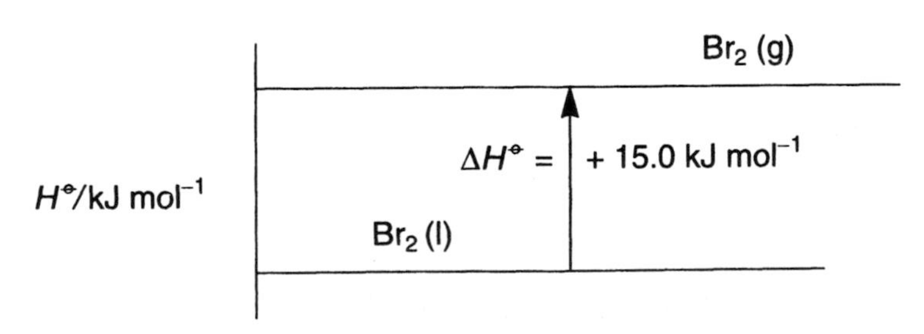

Q2 Is the vaporisation of bromine exothermic or endothermic?

A2 Endothermic.

Q3 If energy is supplied to the system, in what direction does the equilibrium shift?

A3 The position of equilibrium shifts to the right to produce more bromine gas.

Q4 Explain your answer to question 3 using Le Chatelier's principle.

A4 The system absorbs the added energy in an endothermic reaction, i.e. by vaporising some bromine.

Q5 Explain what happens when this system, at equilibrium, is cooled.

A5 When the system is cooled, it loses energy. The system responds by releasing energy in an exothermic reaction, i.e. by condensing some bromine.

Note that for equilibrium systems, $\Delta H^\ominus$ values are quoted for the reaction as written from left to right (the forward reaction). The reverse reaction has the same numerical value of $\Delta H^\ominus$, but with the opposite sign.

If it is available, watch the second part of the ILPAC video programme 'Equilibrium', which deals with the effect of temperature on another equilibrium system. Be ready to make notes summarising the experiments. If necessary you could also watch the third part, which deals with the effect of pressure, but it would be better to leave this until later.

To consolidate your understanding of the effect of temperature on equilibrium systems, read the appropriate section of your textbook(s). Look for a simple qualitative account; don't worry about the **extent** of the shift in equilibrium position. If you have not seen the video look for an account of the effect of temperature on the equilibrium system:

$$N_2O_4\,(g) \rightleftharpoons 2NO_2\,(g); \quad \Delta H^\ominus = +57.2 \text{ kJ mol}^{-1}$$

You should now be able to do the following exercises in which you apply what you have learned to chemical equilibria.

EXERCISE 9

Answers on page 78

A sealed syringe, with a free-moving piston, containing an equilibrium mixture of nitrogen dioxide, NO_2, and dinitrogen tetroxide, N_2O_4, at room temperature is immersed first in hot water and then in cold water. Describe the colour changes you would observe and explain them in terms of Le Chatelier's principle.

EXERCISE 10

Answers on page 79

What effect does an increase in temperature have on the position of equilibrium in the following examples:

a $H_2O\,(g) + C\,(s) \rightleftharpoons CO\,(g) + H_2\,(g); \quad \Delta H^\ominus = +13 \text{ kJ mol}^{-1}$
b $H_2O_2\,(l) \rightleftharpoons H_2\,(g) + O_2\,(g); \quad \Delta H^\ominus = +210 \text{ kJ mol}^{-1}$
c $C\,(s) + O_2\,(g) \rightleftharpoons CO_2\,(g); \quad \Delta H^\ominus = -393.5 \text{ kJ mol}^{-1}$
d $Hg\,(l) \rightleftharpoons Hg\,(g); \quad \Delta H^\ominus = +60.84 \text{ kJ mol}^{-1}$
e $AgClO_2\,(s) \rightleftharpoons Ag\,(s) + \frac{1}{2}Cl_2\,(g) + O_2\,(g); \quad \Delta H^\ominus = 0.0 \text{ kJ mol}^{-1}$.

EXERCISE 11

Answers on page 79

Write four sentences summarising the effect of:

a an increase of temperature on
  i) an exothermic reaction,
  ii) an endothermic reaction;
b a decrease of temperature on
  i) an exothermic reaction,
  ii) an endothermic reaction.

Having discussed what happens to equilibrium systems when the temperature changes, we now consider changes in pressure.

3.6 The effect on equilibrium of changing pressure

OBJECTIVE When you have finished this section you should be able to:

- apply Le Chatelier's principle to the effect on equilibria of **changing pressure.**

The effect of changing pressure is illustrated for systems where gases are involved. We choose gaseous systems to illustrate this because solid and liquid components are virtually unaffected by pressure; their volumes, and hence concentrations, are unaltered. However, in reactions involving gases, an increase in pressure brings the molecules closer together and thus increases the concentration of the gaseous components.

If you have not yet seen the third part of the ILPAC video programme 'Equilibrium', which illustrates by experiment the effect on an equilibrium system of changing the pressure, do so now if this is possible.

Read about the effects of pressure changes on equilibrium systems to help you with the exercises which follow. Again, focus on a qualitative account; leave any calculations until later.

After working through the following Revealing Exercise you should be able to explain how a gaseous system in equilibrium responds to a change in pressure which is imposed externally.

The system we will use is:

$$PCl_5\ (g) \rightleftharpoons PCl_3\ (g) + Cl_2\ (g)$$

A mixture of PCl_5, PCl_3 and Cl_2 was placed in a glass syringe, the nozzle was sealed, and the system was allowed to reach equilibrium at 250°C (Fig. 10).

Figure 10

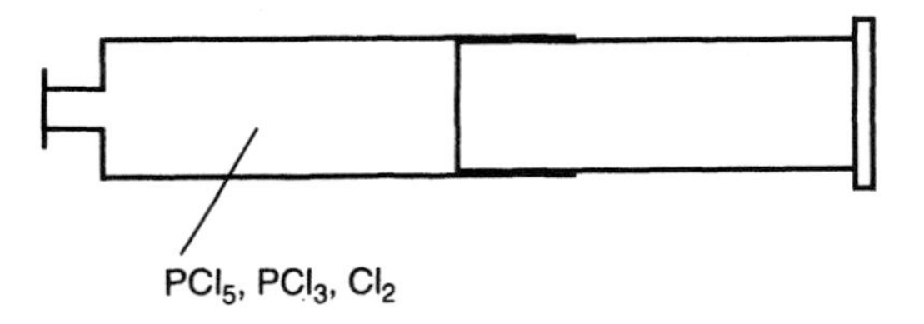

The pressure of the system was increased by moving the plunger in (Fig. 11). The temperature was kept at 250°C.

Figure 11

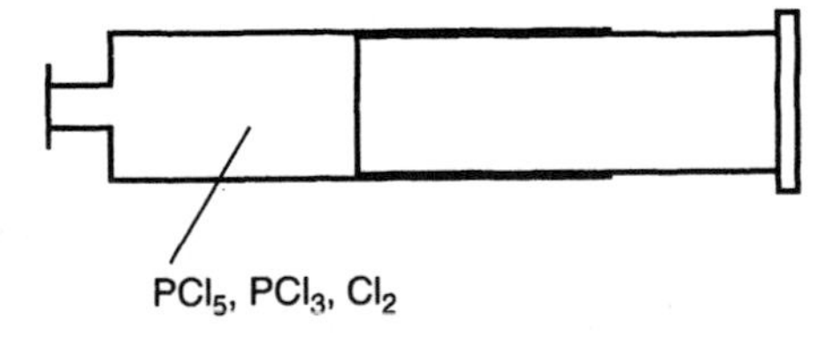

EXERCISE *Revealing*

Q1 According to Le Chatelier's principle, how will this system react to the increased pressure?

A1 It will shift in such a way that the pressure will decrease towards the original pressure.

Q2 How many moles appear on the right-hand side of the equation?

A2 Two.

Q3 How many moles appear on the left-hand side of the equation?

A3 One.

Q4 At the same temperature and volume, which will exert less pressure: one mole of gas or two moles of gas?

A4 One mole of gas.

Q5 Which reaction (forward or reverse) lowers the pressure?

A5 The reverse reaction lowers the pressure:

$$PCl_3 \text{ (g)} + Cl_2 \text{ (g)} \rightarrow PCl_5 \text{ (g)}$$

Q6 How would the system shown in Fig. 11 respond to an increase in volume caused by pulling the plunger out a short distance? Assume that the temperature remains constant.

A6 An increase in volume would cause a decrease in the pressure. The system would tend to increase the pressure by shifting to the right, thus producing a greater number of molecules.

The important idea to remember in connection with gaseous equilibria is that the pressure of a gas is proportional to the number of molecules (or amount) present. The reaction which results in fewer molecules being formed will reduce the pressure of the system and so oppose an applied increase in pressure.

Now try the following exercises. The first deals with homogeneous systems and the second with heterogeneous systems.

EXERCISE 12
Answers on page 79

What is the effect on the position of equilibrium of increasing the pressure in the following systems?

a $N_2 \text{ (g)} + 3H_2 \text{ (g)} \rightleftharpoons 2NH_3 \text{ (g)}$
b $2SO_2 \text{ (g)} + O_2 \text{ (g)} \rightleftharpoons 2SO_3 \text{ (g)}$
c $2HI \text{ (g)} \rightleftharpoons H_2 \text{ (g)} + I_2 \text{ (g)}$.

EXERCISE 13
Answers on page 79

What is the effect on the position of equilibrium of decreasing the pressure in the following systems?

a $3Fe \text{ (s)} + 4H_2O \text{ (g)} \rightleftharpoons Fe_3O_4 \text{ (s)} + 4H_2 \text{ (g)}$
b $S \text{ (s)} + O_2 \text{ (g)} \rightleftharpoons SO_2 \text{ (g)}$
c $CaCO_3 \text{ (s)} \rightleftharpoons CaO \text{ (s)} + CO_2 \text{ (g)}$.

EXERCISE 14
Answers on page 79

Copy the following statements in your notebook and complete them.

a The only components of an equilibrium system to be affected by changes in pressure are those in the .... state.
b If pressure is applied to an equilibrium mixture involving gases, the position of equilibrium shifts in such a way as to cause a(n) .... in the number of molecules.

c If the pressure on an equilibrium mixture involving gases is reduced, the equilibrium shifts in such a way as to cause a(n) .... in the number of molecules.

d If a system has .... number of gas molecules on either side of the equation, increasing or decreasing the pressure of this system has no effect on the equilibrium position.

We now come to the last of the four factors affecting equilibrium.

3.7 The effect on equilibrium of catalysts

OBJECTIVES

When you have finished this section you should be able to:

- state the effect of **catalysts** on equilibrium systems;
- discuss the factors affecting equilibrium in some **industrial processes**.

Catalysts are often used in industrial processes which involve equilibrium systems; you have met several examples in your pre-A-level course, such as the Haber process for manufacturing ammonia and the contact process for manufacturing sulphuric acid.

Industrial chemists obviously want a high yield of product, and will therefore consider all the factors which shift the equilibrium position to the right. They must also consider the rate at which equilibrium is achieved and the cost of shifting the equilibrium position.

Read about catalysts and equilibrium systems, distinguishing carefully between the effect on the **position of equilibrium** and the effect on the **rate of achieving equilibrium**. You may find it helpful to look at sections covering the **Haber process**, the **contact process** and the **Bosch process**, which are mentioned in the next exercise.

Now you should be able to put together all the principles you have learned so far in this book and apply them to some industrial processes.

EXERCISE 15
Answers on page 79

Consider the following equilibrium systems used in industrial processes.

a Contact process:

$$2SO_2\,(g) + O_2\,(g) \rightleftharpoons 2SO_3\,(g);\quad \Delta H^{\ominus} = -97\ \text{kJ mol}^{-1}$$

b Haber process:

$$N_2\,(g) + 3H_2\,(g) \rightleftharpoons 2NH_3\,(g);\quad \Delta H^{\ominus} = -92\ \text{kJ mol}^{-1}$$

c Bosch process:

$$C\,(s) + H_2O\,(g) \rightleftharpoons CO\,(g) + H_2\,(g);\quad \Delta H^{\ominus} = +131\ \text{kJ mol}^{-1}$$

In each case state the effect of a catalyst (if one is used) on the equilibrium system, and the conditions of temperature and pressure (high or low) which give the highest yield of product (s) in the equilibrium mixture.

You may have realised that the conditions which give the highest yield of product in an equilibrium mixture are not always those used in practice. We ask you to explain this in the next exercise. Use your textbook(s) again if necessary.

EXERCISE 16
Answers on page 79

a Both the contact and Haber processes are run at moderately high temperatures despite the fact that lower temperatures give more products in the equilibrium mixtures. Explain.

b Why is the contact process not run at high pressure?

c Why is the Bosch process not run at a pressure lower than atmospheric pressure?

Part A test

To find out how well you have learned the material in Part A, try the test which follows. Read the notes below before starting:

1. You should spend about 60 minutes on this test.
2. Hand your answers to your teacher for marking.

Directions In questions 1 and 2, **one** or **more** of the suggested responses is correct. Answer as follows:
A if **1, 2** and **3** are all correct,
B if **1** and **2** only are correct,
C if **2** and **3** only are correct,
D if **1** only is correct,
E if **3** only is correct.

Directions summarised				
A	B	C	D	E
1, 2, 3	**1, 2**	**2, 3**	**1**	**3**
correct	only	only	only	only

1. Which of the following changes would produce an increased yield of the ester in the reaction:

$$CH_3CO_2H\ (l) + C_2H_5OH\ (l) \rightleftharpoons CH_3CO_2C_2H_5\ (l) + H_2O\ (l)$$

1 More ethanol is added.
2 The reaction is carried out in an inert solvent.
3 H^+ ions are added to catalyse the reaction. (1)

2. When sulphur dioxide is converted into sulphur trioxide during the manufacture of sulphuric acid, the reaction is usually carried out at atmospheric pressure because
1 a good yield of sulphur trioxide is obtained at this pressure,
2 the reaction is unaffected by pressure changes,
3 increased pressure makes the catalyst used in this stage less effective. (1)

3. **a** Illustrate the four characteristics of the equilibrium state by reference to the equilibrium system:

$$2HI\ (g) \rightleftharpoons H_2\ (g) + I_2\ (g)$$ (7)

b It can be shown that if some solid radioactive iodine is added to the system:

$$I_2\ (s) \rightleftharpoons I_2\ (g)$$

the iodine vapour also becomes radioactive. Why is this? (2)

4. Consider the system:

$$Fe\ (s) + 4H_2O\ (g) \rightleftharpoons Fe_3O_4\ (s) + 4H_2\ (g); \quad \Delta H^{\circ} = +151\ kJ\ mol^{-1}$$

With reference to Le Chatelier's principle, **explain** the effect (if any) on the yield of hydrogen of:
a increasing the temperature,
b increasing the total pressure,

c adding more iron,
d increasing the partial pressure of the steam. (8)

5. A solution of antimony trichloride, $SbCl_3$, is made by dissolving solid antimony trichloride in 6 M hydrochloric acid; under these conditions the following equilibrium lies far to the left:

$$SbCl_3\ (aq) + H_2O\ (l) \rightleftharpoons SbClO\ (s) + 2HCl\ (aq)$$

a Why is the solution prepared using 6 M HCl? (2)
b What would be observed if
i) the solution were diluted,
ii) solid sodium hydroxide were added? (2)

6. The main starting material for the industrial production of ethanol is ethene. The ethene undergoes direct catalytic hydration:

$$CH_2{=}CH_2\ (g) + H_2O\ (g) \rightarrow C_2H_5OH\ (g); \quad \Delta H^{\ominus} = -46\ \text{kJ mol}^{-1}$$

The process is generally operated at around 6 MPa pressure and at a temperature of 300°C. The gases are passed over a phosphoric acid catalyst when about 5% of the reactants are converted into ethanol.

a i) Explain, in terms of Le Chatelier's principle, why the formation of ethanol is favoured by very high pressure. (2)
ii) Give **two** disadvantages of operating the process at very high pressure. (2)
b i) Explain, in terms of Le Chatelier's principle, why a low temperature favours the production of ethanol. (2)
ii) Why are low temperatures not used in practice? (1)

(Total: 30 marks)

QUANTITATIVE ASPECTS OF EQUILIBRIUM

In this book you have so far met examples of several different equilibrium systems and investigated the effect of changing the conditions at equilibrium. These effects were described qualitatively by Le Chatelier's principle; we now consider them quantitatively by using the equilibrium law.

THE EQUILIBRIUM LAW

The equilibrium law applies to all equilibrium systems and we shall use it as a tool to make precise mathematical predictions and calculations. It was put forward as a result of careful experimental work, but has a firm basis in theoretical thermodynamics.

4.1 Writing an equilibrium law expression

OBJECTIVES When you have finished this section you should be able to:

- state **the equilibrium law;**
- apply the law to any reversible reaction by writing an expression for the **equilibrium constant,** K_c.

Scan the section of your textbook which covers the equilibrium law. Look for a mathematical expression which relates the concentrations of the components in a system at equilibrium.

What will probably not be mentioned in your textbook is the fact that although the equilibrium constants K_c and K_p may express the equilibrium condition, they are not truly constant!

For any reversible reaction the **thermodynamic** equilibrium constant K, which **is** constant at constant temperature, is expressed in terms of 'relative activities' instead of concentration or partial pressures.

The 'relative activity' of a substance is a measure of the 'effective concentration' of that substance. In other words, although a substance A in a mixture may have a concentration [A], it may behave as if its concentration were somewhat less than [A], owing to molecular or ionic interactions.

If we restrict ourselves to systems where these interactions are small, such as gases at low pressure, covalent liquids or, in the case of ionic substances, solutions in which ionic concentration is low, then K_p and K_c will be reasonably constant (at constant temperature). Thus for GCE A-level work we may use K_p and K_c as expressions of the equilibrium condition, but, in the light of the above, we should rarely be justified in calculating values to more than two, or at most three, significant figures.

We now show you, in a Worked Example, how to write an equilibrium law expression for a particular equilibrium system. We illustrate the conventions used in writing equilibrium law expressions and show you how to work out the unit of K_c.

WORKED EXAMPLE

a Write an expression for K_c for the reaction

$$N_2O_4\,(g) \rightleftharpoons 2NO_2\,(g)$$

b What is the unit of K_c in this case? Assume the unit of concentration is mol dm^{-3}.

Solution

a By convention, the equilibrium law is written with the products in the numerator and the reactants in the denominator; the index (exponent) of the concentration term is the same as the stoichiometric coefficient in the balanced equation:

$$K_c = \frac{[NO_2\,(g)]^2_{eqm}}{[N_2O_4\,(g)]_{eqm}}$$

In future, we assume that the concentrations used in equilibrium law expressions are equilibrium ones and we leave out the subscript 'eqm'. This saves space and looks neater on the page. So the above expression becomes:

$$K_c = \frac{[NO_2\,(g)]^2}{[N_2O_4\,(g)]}$$

Warning note! You would be wise to include the subscripts 'eqm' in your answers to examination questions. One examination board, for example, will award full marks only if such subscripts are included in the answers.

b To work out the unit, assume that

$$[NO_2\,(g)] = x \text{ mol dm}^{-3} \text{ and } [N_2O_4\,(g)] = y \text{ mol dm}^{-3}$$

Substitution into the equilibrium law gives:

$$K_c = \frac{(x \text{ mol dm}^{-3})^2}{y \text{ mol dm}^{-3}} = \frac{x^2}{y}\frac{(\text{mol dm}^{-3})^2}{\text{mol dm}^{-3}} = \frac{x^2}{y} \text{ mol dm}^{-3}$$

Now try writing some equilibrium law expressions by doing the next exercise.

EXERCISE 17

Answers on page 79

a For each of the following reactions write an expression for K_c. Work out units for K_c and include them in your answers, assuming that concentrations are measured in mol dm^{-3}.

i) $2HBr\,(g) \rightleftharpoons H_2\,(g) + Br_2\,(g)$,
ii) $2SO_2\,(g) + O_2\,(g) \rightleftharpoons 2SO_3\,(g)$,
iii) $Cu(NH_3)_4^{2+}\,(aq) \rightleftharpoons Cu^{2+}\,(aq) + 4NH_3\,(aq)$,
iv) $2NO\,(g) + O_2\,(g) \rightleftharpoons 2NO_2\,(g)$,
v) $4PF_5\,(g) \rightleftharpoons P_4\,(g) + 10F_2\,(g)$,
vi) $2NO\,(g) \rightleftharpoons N_2\,(g) + O_2\,(g)$,
vii) $C_2H_5OH\,(l) + CH_3CO_2H\,(l) \rightleftharpoons CH_3CO_2C_2H_5\,(l) + H_2O\,(l)$.

b Look at the examples in which K_c has no unit. What do all these reactions have in common?

As soon as you come to consider **numerical values** of K_c, you must remember two important points.

1. A particular value of K_c refers only to one particular temperature.
2. The form of the equilibrium law expression (and therefore the value of K_c) depends on the way the equation is written.

We illustrate these ideas in the following exercises.

EXERCISE 18
Answers on page 80

The same equilibrium system may be represented by two different equations:

$$COCl_2\ (g) \rightleftharpoons CO\ (g) + Cl_2\ (g)$$

$$CO\ (g) + Cl_2\ (g) \rightleftharpoons COCl_2\ (g)$$

a Write expressions for two equilibrium constants, K_c and K_c'.
b What is the mathematical relation between K_c and K_c'?

EXERCISE 19
Answers on page 80

The equilibrium between dinitrogen tetroxide and nitrogen dioxide may be represented equally well by two different equations:

$$\tfrac{1}{2}N_2O_4\ (g) \rightleftharpoons NO_2\ (g)$$
$$N_2O_4\ (g) \rightleftharpoons 2NO_2\ (g)$$

a Write expressions for two equilibrium constants, K_c and K_c'.
b At 100°C, $K_c' = 0.490\ \text{mol dm}^{-3}$ and at 200°C, $K_c' = 18.6\ \text{mol dm}^{-3}$. What are the values of K_c at these temperatures?

4.2 Calculating the value of an equilibrium constant

OBJECTIVE

When you have finished this section you should be able to:

- calculate a value for an **equilibrium constant** by direct substitution of equilibrium concentrations into the equilibrium law.

We illustrate the method of calculation by a Worked Example.

WORKED EXAMPLE

Equilibrium was established at 308 K for the system

$$CO\ (g) + Br_2\ (g) \rightleftharpoons COBr_2\ (g)$$

Analysis of the mixture gave the following values of concentration:

$$[CO\ (g)] = 8.78 \times 10^{-3}\ \text{mol dm}^{-3}$$

$$[Br_2\ (g)] = 4.90 \times 10^{-3}\ \text{mol dm}^{-3}$$

$$[COBr_2\ (g)] = 3.40 \times 10^{-3}\ \text{mol dm}^{-3}$$

Calculate the value of the equilibrium constant.

Solution

1. Write the equilibrium law expression for this reaction in terms of concentration:

$$K_c = \frac{[COBr_2\ (g)]}{[CO\ (g)][Br_2\ (g)]}$$

2. Substitute the equilibrium concentrations:

$$K_c = \frac{3.40 \times 10^{-3}\ \text{mol dm}^{-3}}{8.78 \times 10^{-3}\ \text{mol dm}^{-3} \times 4.90 \times 10^{-3}\ \text{mol dm}^{-3}}$$

3. Do the arithmetic; cancel units where appropriate.

$$K_c = 79.0 \text{ dm}^3 \text{ mol}^{-1}$$

Now try a similar problem.

EXERCISE 20
Answers on page 80

The equilibrium

$$N_2O_4 \rightleftharpoons 2NO_2$$

can be established in an inert solvent at 298 K. Analysis of an equilibrium mixture gave the concentration of N_2O_4 as 0.021 mol dm^{-3} and the concentration of NO_2 as 0.010 mol dm^{-3}. Calculate the value of the equilibrium constant at 298 K.

If you need more practice in this type of calculation, try some of the problems in Appendix A1.1 on page 66.

In some problems, you may have to calculate concentrations from amounts and total volume before you apply the equilibrium law. Try this in the next exercise.

EXERCISE 21
Answers on page 80

Some phosphorus pentachloride was heated at 250°C in a sealed container until equilibrium was reached according to the equation

$$PCl_5 \text{ (g)} \rightleftharpoons PCl_3 \text{ (g)} + Cl_2 \text{ (g)}$$

Analysis of the mixture showed that it contained 0.0042 mol of PCl_5, 0.040 mol of PCl_3 and 0.040 mol of Cl_2. The total volume was 2.0 dm^3.

a Calculate the concentration of each component and hence determine the equilibrium constant, K_c.

b The value of K_c for this system is much greater than the one you calculated in Exercise 20. What can you say about the relative concentrations of reactants and products when
i) K_c is very large,
ii) K_c is very small?

Sometimes you can simplify a calculation by omitting the volume from the equilibrium law expression, as we now show.

4.3 When volume can be omitted from an equilibrium law expression

OBJECTIVE

When you have finished this section you should be able to:

- recognise those systems for which the equilibrium law expression is independent of the volume.

In the next exercise you show that, for an equilibrium system where the equilibrium constant has no unit, amounts can be used directly in the equilibrium law expression without using the total volume.

EXERCISE 22

Answers on page 81

The table below shows the composition of two equilibrium mixtures at 485°C.

	Amount of H_2/mol	Amount of I_2/mol	Amount of HI/mol
1	0.02265	0.02840	0.1715
2	0.01699	0.04057	0.1779

a Write the equation for the formation of hydrogen iodide from hydrogen and iodine.
b Write an expression for the equilibrium constant, K_c.
c Calculate a value of K_c for each mixture, assuming the volume of the equilibrium mixture is 1.00 dm^3. Include units in your working.
d For mixture 1, calculate a value for the equilibrium constant, assuming the volume is 2.00 dm^3.
e For mixture 2, calculate a value for the equilibrium constant, assuming the volume is V dm^3. Show that the volume cancels.

Exercise 22 should convince you that the volume of the reaction mixture made no difference to the value of the equilibrium constant. We can generalise this for gaseous reactions and reactions in solution: if the equation shows equal numbers of molecules on both sides, then the equilibrium law expression is independent of the volume, and K_c is unitless.

In these circumstances, to calculate an equilibrium constant you can use equilibrium amounts rather than concentrations; or you can include V as an unknown value which cancels as in Exercise 22**e**.

In the next experiment you calculate an equilibrium constant, using concentrations determined by titration. If you have already done part (a) of the experiment, and at least 48 hours have elapsed since you prepared the mixtures, read again the Aim and Introduction sections and then proceed to part (b).

EXPERIMENT 2 Determining an equilibrium constant

Aim The purpose of this experiment is to calculate the equilibrium constant for the reaction:

$$\underset{\text{ethyl ethanoate}}{CH_3CO_2C_2H_5\,(l)} + \underset{\text{water}}{H_2O\,(l)} \rightleftharpoons \underset{\text{ethanol}}{C_2H_5OH\,(l)} + \underset{\text{ethanoic acid}}{CH_3CO_2H\,(l)}$$

Introduction The reaction between ethyl ethanoate and water is very slow. However, by using a catalyst, dilute hydrochloric acid, equilibrium can be attained in about 48 hours.

In part (a) of the experiment you prepare, in sealed containers, mixtures containing different proportions of the two reactants. To each mixture you add a fixed amount of dilute hydrochloric acid as a catalyst.

In part (b), after the mixtures have reached equilibrium at room temperature, you analyse each one by titration with sodium hydroxide. Part of the added sodium hydroxide reacts with the catalyst; the rest indicates the amount of ethanoic acid in the equilibrium mixture.

Finally, from the starting amounts and the amount of ethanoic acid produced, you calculate the equilibrium amounts of all four components and use them to determine the equilibrium constant.

Requirements – Part (a)

- safety spectacles
- 5 specimen tubes with well-fitting caps
- labels for tubes and stoppers
- access to a balance (sensitivity ± 0.01 g or better)
- pipette, 5 cm^3, and safety filler
- dilute hydrochloric acid, 2 M HCl
- 2 measuring cylinders, 10 cm^3 (one must be dry)
- ethyl ethanoate, $CH_3CO_2C_2H_5$
- distilled water

Procedure – Part (a)

1. Label five specimen tubes with your name and the date. Number them 1a, 1b, 2, 3 and 4. Number the stoppers too, so that they do not get misplaced.
2. Weigh each tube, with its stopper, and record the masses in a copy of Results Table 2.
3. Using a pipette and safety filler, carefully add 5.0 cm^3 of 2 M hydrochloric acid to each tube, replacing the stoppers as you go. The volume of acid must be precisely the same in each tube; measure it as carefully as you can. If you think you have made a mistake, wash out the tube, dry it and start again.
4. Weigh each stoppered tube in turn and record the masses.
5. Select a **dry** measuring cylinder, and use it to add to tubes 2, 3 and 4 the volumes (approximate) of ethyl ethanoate shown in Results Table 2, again replacing the stoppers as you go.
6. Weigh the stoppered tubes 2, 3 and 4. Record the masses.
7. From a second measuring cylinder, add to tubes 3 and 4 the volumes (approximate) of distilled water shown in Results Table 2, again replacing the stoppers as you go.
8. Weigh the stoppered tubes 3 and 4. Record the masses.
9. Gently shake the tubes and set them aside for at least 48 hours. During this time, arrange to shake the tubes occasionally.

HAZARD WARNING

Ethyl ethanoate is flammable. Therefore you **must**:

- keep the stopper on the bottle as much as possible;
- keep the liquid away from a naked flame.

Hydrochloric acid is an irritant.

Results Table 2

Tube number	1a	1b	2	3	4
Mass of empty tube/g					
Volume of HCl (aq) added/cm^3	5.0	5.0	5.0	5.0	5.0
Mass of tube after addition/g					
Volume of ethyl ethanoate added/cm^3	–	–	5.0	4.0	2.0
Mass of tube after addition/g					
Volume of water added/cm^3	–	–	–	1.0	3.0
Mass of tube after addition/g					
Mass of ethyl ethanoate added/g					
Mass of HCl (aq) added/g					
Mass of water added/g					

In addition to the two tubes containing only hydrochloric acid, you now have three tubes containing different amounts of ethyl ethanoate and water (tube 2 has water from the acid). When these mixtures have reached equilibrium, you can analyse them in part (b) of the experiment.

Before you begin part (b), revise the technique of titration (ILPAC Volume 1, The Mole, Experiment 3). You may find it helpful to have another look at the ILPAC video programme 'Performing a titration'.

Requirements – Part (b)

- safety spectacles
- 5 conical flasks, 250 cm^3
- wash bottle of distilled water
- phenolphthalein indicator
- burette, stand and white tile
- small funnel
- sodium hydroxide solution, 1 M NaOH (standardised) (**warning:** corrosive)

Procedure – Part (b)

1. Rinse and fill a burette with standardised sodium hydroxide solution.
2. Carefully pour the contents of tube 1a into a conical flask. Rinse the tube into the flask three times with distilled water.
3. Add two to three drops of phenolphthalein indicator solution and titrate the acid against sodium hydroxide solution. Record your burette readings in a copy of Results Table 3.
4. Repeat steps 2 and 3 for each of the other tubes in turn. Remember that tube 1b should require the same volume of alkali as tube 1a, but the others should require a little more. Complete Results Table 3.

Results Table 3

Solution in flask	Equilibrium mixture				
Solution in burette	Sodium hydroxide			mol dm^{-3}	
Indicator	Phenolphthalein				
Tube number	1a	1b	2	3	4
Final burette reading					
Initial burette reading					
Titre/cm^3					

Calculations

The calculations seem complex, but consist of several very simple steps. The flow scheme below summarises the procedure; refer to it as you work through so that you can see the purpose of each step.

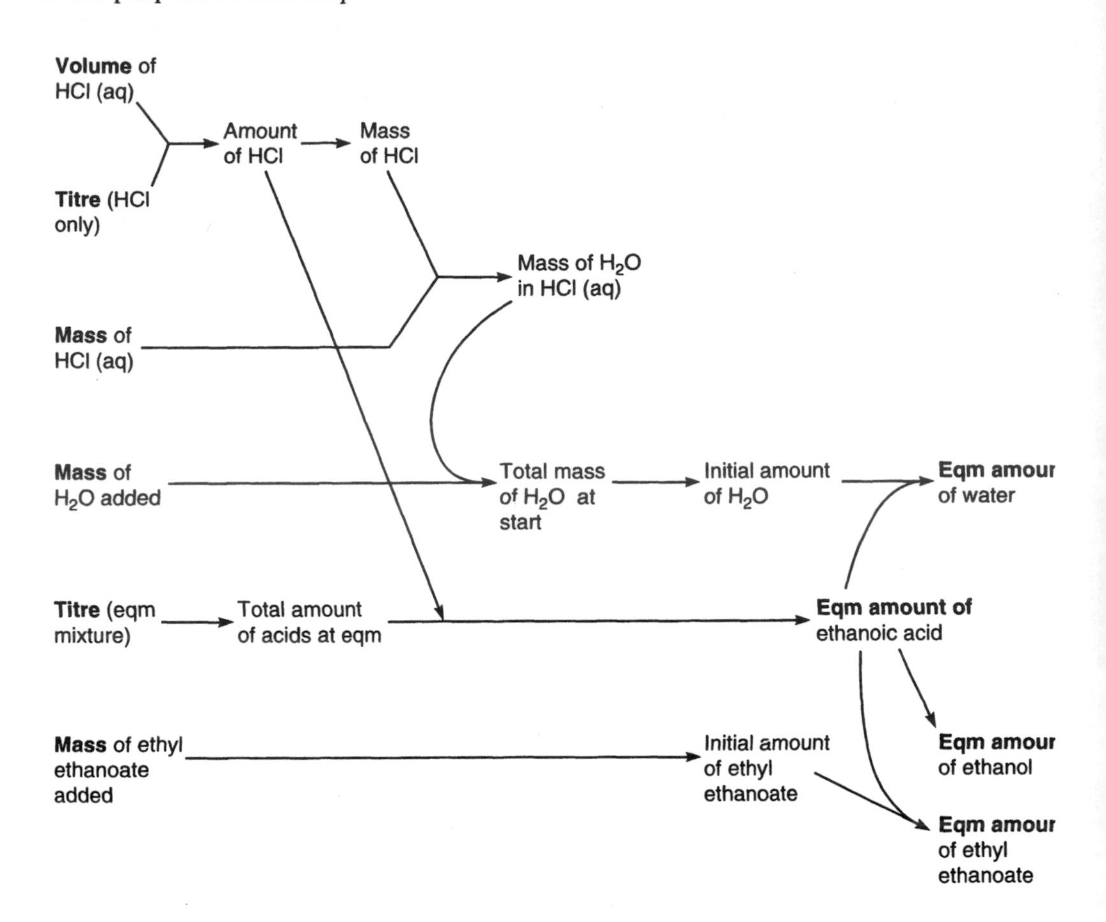

1. From the average titre for tubes 1a and 1b (or the better titre if you think one was inaccurate), calculate the amount of hydrochloric acid catalyst you added to each of the five tubes. Remember that hydrochloric acid and sodium hydroxide react in equimolar amounts and that

$$\text{amount} = \text{concentration} \times \text{volume}.$$

   Record this amount in each column of a copy of Results Table 4.
2. From the titres for tubes 2, 3 and 4 in turn, calculate and record the total amount of acid (hydrochloric and ethanoic) in each mixture.
3. Calculate, by subtraction, the amount of ethanoic acid in each equilibrium mixture. This is the first of the four quantities you need to substitute in the equilibrium law expression. Complete the third row of Results Table 4.
4. The equation for the equilibrium system shows that the amount of ethanol produced is equal to the amount of ethanoic acid produced. You now have the second of the four quantities you need. Complete the fourth row of your table.
5. From the data in Results Table 2, calculate the amount of ethyl ethanoate added to each tube

$$\text{amount of ethyl ethanoate} = \frac{\text{mass after addition} - \text{mass before addition}}{\text{molar mass}}$$

   Complete the fifth row of your table.

6. Calculate and record the equilibrium amount of ethyl ethanoate in each tube, using the relationship:

$$\text{eqm amount of } CH_3CO_2C_2H_5 = \text{initial amount of } CH_3CO_2C_2H_5 - \text{eqm amount of } CH_3CO_2H$$

You can see from the chemical equation that the amount of ethyl ethanoate which reacts is equal to the amount of ethanoic acid produced. You now have the third of the four quantities you need.

7. Calculate and record the mass of **pure** HCl in each mixture

$$\text{mass} = \text{amount} \times \text{molar mass}$$

8. Calculate and record the mass of water in the **aqueous** HCl added to each tube. (You need to refer back to Results Table 2)

$$\text{mass of water} = \text{mass of HCl (aq)} - \text{mass of HCl}$$

9. Calculate and record the total amount of water initially in each mixture

$$\text{initial amount of } H_2O = \frac{\text{mass in HCl (aq)} + \text{mass added}}{\text{molar mass}}$$

10. Calculate and record the equilibrium amount of water in each mixture

$$\text{eqm amount of } H_2O = \text{initial amount of } H_2O - \text{eqm amount of } CH_3CO_2H$$

11. Write an equilibrium law expression for the reaction and calculate three values of the equilibrium constant, K_c.

Results Table 4

Tube number		2	3	4
1.	Amount of HCl/mol			
2.	Total amount of acid at eqm/mol			
3.	Eqm amount of ethanoic acid/mol			
4.	Eqm amount of ethanol/mol			
5.	Initial amount of ethyl ethanoate/mol			
6.	Eqm amount of ethyl ethanoate/mol			
7.	Mass of pure HCl/g			
8.	Mass of water in HCl (aq)/g			
9.	Initial amount of water/mol			
10.	Eqm amount of water/mol			
11.	Eqm constant, K_c			

(Specimen results on page 82.)

Discuss the results of this experiment with other members of your class and your teacher.

Questions

Answers on page 82

1. In step 2 of part (b) some more water (one of the reactants) is added to the mixture. Furthermore, titration of the equilibrium mixture with sodium hydroxide neutralises both the catalyst acid and the ethanoic acid. In other words, one of the products is removed.
   Use Le Chatelier's principle to predict what effect these procedures should have on the equilibrium position.
2. It seems that analysis of the equilibrium mixture by this titration does not in fact disturb the equilibrium to any noticeable extent. Can you explain this?

As has been stated earlier, calculations for this experiment may seem complex but the chore of working through them can be avoided by using a computer 'spreadsheet'. You may be able to do this if a computer and the appropriate software are available. Ask your teacher for details.

You should not, however, use a spreadsheet as an easy way out and it is important that you should understand the outline of the calculations. It can be explained thus:

for the equilibrium

	$CH_3CO_2C_2H_5$ +	H_2O ⇌	CH_3CO_2H +	C_2H_5OH
Initial amounts	a	b	c	d
Equilibrium amounts	$a-x$	$b-x$	$c+x$	$d+x$

$$K_c = \frac{(c+x)\,(d+x)}{(a-x)\,(b-x)}$$

The initial amounts a, b, c and d are obtained from the masses of the substances. The equilibrium amount of ethanoic acid $(c + x)$ is found by titration, which means that we can now find the value of x and so work out the equilibrium amounts of the other three compounds. Complications arise because (a) the titration determines the **total** acid and we have to allow for the catalyst, hence the 'blank' determination and (b) the hydrochloric acid contains water, the amount of which has to be calculated and included in the initial amount.

You have done several direct calculations of equilibrium constants using the equilibrium law. In the next section we show you how to use the equilibrium law in a variety of other calculations.

■ 4.4 Various numerical problems involving equilibrium constants

We describe different types of problem by means of objectives and illustrate them by Worked Examples and exercises.

OBJECTIVE

When you have finished this section you should be able to:

- calculate the equilibrium concentration of one substance in a mixture, given the equilibrium concentrations of all other substances, the balanced equation and the value of the equilibrium constant, K_c.

WORKED EXAMPLE

For the equilibrium:

$$PCl_5\,(g) \rightleftharpoons PCl_3\,(g) + Cl_2\,(g)$$

$$K_c = 0.19\ \text{mol dm}^{-3}\ \text{at}\ 250°\text{C}.$$

One equilibrium mixture at this temperature contains PCl_5 at a concentration of 0.20 mol dm^{-3} and PCl_3 at a concentration of 0.010 mol dm^{-3}.
Calculate the concentration of Cl_2 in this mixture.

Solution

1. Start by writing the equation (even if it is given in the question). Leave space where the equilibrium concentrations can be tabulated under the formulae of the compounds:

$$PCl_5\ (g) \rightleftharpoons PCl_3\ (g) + Cl_2\ (g)$$

Equilibrium
concn/mol dm^{-3}

2. Indicate the equilibrium concentrations under the equation. Let the concentration of chlorine, $[Cl_2\ (g)]$, be x mol dm^{-3}

	PCl_5 (g)	⇌ PCl_3 (g)	+ Cl_2 (g)
Equilibrium concn/mol dm^3	0.20	0.010	x

3. Write the equilibrium law expression in terms of concentration

$$K_c = \frac{[PCl_3\ (g)]\,[Cl_2\ (g)]}{[PCl_5\ (g)]}$$

4. Substitute all values into the expression (remember to include units).

$$0.19 \text{ mol dm}^{-3} = \frac{0.010 \text{ mol dm}^{-3} \times x \text{ mol dm}^{-3}}{0.20 \text{ mol dm}^{-3}}$$

5. Solve the equation for x:

$$x = \frac{0.19 \times 0.20}{0.010} = 3.8$$

$$\therefore\ [Cl_2\ (g)] = 3.8 \text{ mol dm}^{-3}$$

Now do Exercises 23 and 24.

EXERCISE 23

Answers on page 82

Some N_2O_4 dissolved in trichloromethane was allowed to reach equilibrium at a known temperature

$$N_2O_4 \rightleftharpoons 2NO_2$$

At this point the concentration of NO_2 was 1.85×10^{-3} mol dm^{-3}.
What was the equilibrium concentration of N_2O_4? $K_c = 1.06 \times 10^{-5}$ mol dm^{-3} at this temperature.

EXERCISE 24

Answers on page 83

At 1400 K, $K_c = 2.25 \times 10^{-4}$ mol dm^{-3} for the equilibrium:

$$2H_2S\ (g) \rightleftharpoons 2H_2\ (g) + S_2\ (g)$$

In an equilibrium mixture, $[H_2S\ (g)] = 4.84 \times 10^{-3}$ mol dm^{-3} and $[S_2\ (g)] = 2.33 \times 10^{-3}$ mol dm^{-3}. Calculate the equilibrium concentration of H_2.

There are some more exercises of this type, for extra practice or for revision, in Appendix A1.2 on page 66.

The next exercise is similar, but requires an extra step at the start; i.e. calculating concentrations from amounts and total volume.

EXERCISE 25
Answers on page 83

In another equilibrium mixture of the reaction

$$PCl_5\ (g) \rightleftharpoons PCl_3\ (g) + Cl_2\ (g)$$

at 250°C in a 2.0 dm^3 vessel, there is 0.15 mol of PCl_3 and 0.090 mol of Cl_2. K_c = 0.19 mol dm^{-3} at 250°C.

a Calculate the amount of PCl_5 present at equilibrium.
b Calculate the mass of PCl_5 present at equilibrium.

Don't forget that if the total number of molecules does not change during a homogeneous reaction, the volume doesn't make any difference to the calculation and you need not include it (see page 29).

Now we show you how to apply the equilibrium law to a slightly different type of problem.

OBJECTIVE

When you have finished this section you should be able to:

- calculate the equilibrium constant, K_c, given the balanced equation, the initial concentrations (or amounts) and the equilibrium concentration (or amount) of at least one substance.

WORKED EXAMPLE

6.75 g of SO_2Cl_2 was put into a 2.00 dm^3 vessel, the vessel was sealed and its temperature raised to 375°C. At equilibrium, the vessel contained 0.0345 mol of Cl_2. Calculate the equilibrium constant for the reaction

$$SO_2Cl_2\ (g) \rightleftharpoons SO_2\ (g) + Cl_2\ (g)$$

Solution

1. First, note that the number of molecules **does** change, so you will have to calculate concentrations from amounts.
2. Write the balanced equation, leaving room for initial concentrations above and equilibrium concentrations below:

Initial
concn/mol dm^{-3}

$$SO_2Cl_2\ (g) \rightleftharpoons SO_2\ (g) + Cl_2\ (g)$$

Equilibrium
concn/mol dm^{-3}

3. Calculate the initial concentrations and put the values above the appropriate formulae in the equation.

$$\text{The amount, } n, \text{ of } SO_2Cl_2 = \frac{m}{M} = \frac{6.75\ g}{135\ g\ mol^{-1}} = 0.0500\ mol$$

$$c = \frac{n}{V}$$

$$\therefore\ [SO_2Cl_2\ (g)] = \frac{0.0500\ mol}{2.00\ dm^3} = 0.0250\ mol\ dm^{-3}$$

The initial concentrations of SO_2 and Cl_2 are both zero. Write down the initial concentrations:

Initial concn/mol dm^{-3}	0.025	0	0
	SO_2Cl_2 (g) $\rightleftharpoons$	SO_2 (g) +	Cl_2 (g)
Equilibrium concn/mol dm^{-3}			

4. Now work out the equilibrium concentrations from the data and balanced equation:
   a There is 0.0345 mol of Cl_2 present at equilibrium so there must also be 0.0345 mol of SO_2 present and 0.0345 mol of SO_2Cl_2 must have been present. The concentrations are:

$$[Cl_2\ (g)] = \frac{0.0345\ \text{mol}}{2.00\ \text{dm}^3} = 0.0173\ \text{mol dm}^{-3}$$

$$[SO_2\ (g)] = \frac{0.0345\ \text{mol}}{2.00\ \text{dm}^3} = 0.0173\ \text{mol dm}^{-3}$$

   b The **amount** of SO_2Cl_2 left = initial amount – amount reacted

$$= (0.0500 - 0.0345)\ \text{mol} = 0.0155\ \text{mol}$$

$$\therefore\ [SO_2Cl_2\ (g)] = \frac{0.0155\ \text{mol}}{2.00\ \text{dm}^3} = 0.00775\ \text{mol dm}^{-3}$$

   Write these equilibrium concentrations under the equation:

Initial concn/mol dm^{-3}	0.025	0	0
	SO_2Cl_2 (g) $\rightleftharpoons$	SO_2 (g) +	Cl_2 (g)
Equilibrium concn/mol dm^{-3}	0.00775	0.0173	0.0173

5. From here proceed as in the first worked example. Write the equilibrium law expression and substitute the equilibrium concentrations:

$$K_c = \frac{[SO_2\ (g)]\,[Cl_2\ (g)]}{[SO_2Cl_2\ (g)]}$$

$$= \frac{0.0173\ \text{mol dm}^{-3} \times 0.0173\ \text{mol dm}^{-3}}{0.00775\ \text{mol dm}^{-3}} = \mathbf{0.0386\ mol\ dm^{-3}}$$

Now try the following three exercises, two of which are A-level questions.

EXERCISE 26

Answers on page 83

Ethanoic acid, CH_3CO_2H, and pentene, C_5H_{10}, react to produce pentyl ethanoate in an inert solvent. A solution was prepared containing 0.020 mol of pentene and 0.010 mol of ethanoic acid in 600 cm^3 of solution. At equilibrium there was 9.0×10^{-3} mol of pentyl ethanoate. Calculate the value of K_c from these data.

$$CH_3CO_2H + C_5H_{10} \rightleftharpoons CH_3CO_2C_5H_{11}$$

EXERCISE 27

Answers on page 84

A mixture of 1.90 mol of hydrogen and 1.90 mol of iodine was allowed to reach equilibrium at 710 K. The equilibrium mixture was found to contain 3.00 mol of hydrogen iodide. Calculate the equilibrium constant at 710 K for the reaction

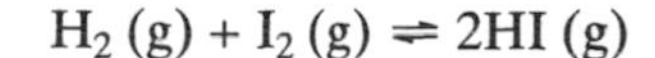

$$H_2\ (g) + I_2\ (g) \rightleftharpoons 2HI\ (g)$$

EXERCISE 28
Answers on page 84

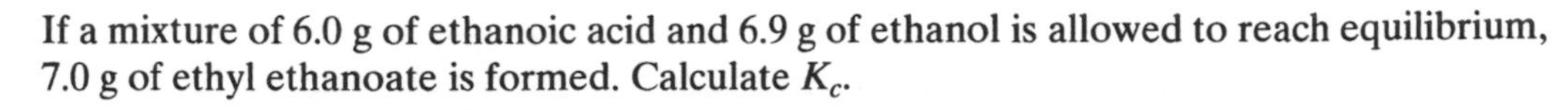
If a mixture of 6.0 g of ethanoic acid and 6.9 g of ethanol is allowed to reach equilibrium, 7.0 g of ethyl ethanoate is formed. Calculate K_c.

$$CH_3CO_2H + C_2H_5OH \rightleftharpoons CH_3CO_2C_2H_5 + H_2O$$

There are some more exercises of this sort, for more practice or for revision, in Appendix A1.3 on page 67.

The type of problem we present in the next section often requires the solution of a quadratic equation, although it is not always possible to tell just by reading the question. The chemistry is usually straightforward, but if you find the mathematics difficult, remember that in an examination you will secure a good proportion of the marks simply by applying the correct principle without actually solving the equation at the last step. In any case, some examining boards rarely set problems which require the solution of quadratic equations.

4.5 Problems involving quadratic equations

The general form of a quadratic equation is

$$ax^2 + bx + c = 0$$

where a, b and c are constants. The solution of this equation is given by the formula

$$x = \frac{-b \pm \sqrt{b^2 - 4ac}}{2a}$$

and it is easy to solve this using a calculator.

OBJECTIVE

When you have finished this section you should be able to:

- **calculate the equilibrium concentrations (or amounts) of substances given the initial concentrations and the value of the equilibrium constant.**

WORKED EXAMPLE

Carbon monoxide and chlorine react to form phosgene, $COCl_2$. A mixture was prepared containing 0.20 mol of CO and 0.10 mol of Cl_2 in a 3.0 dm^3 vessel. At the temperature of the experiment $K_c = 0.410\ dm^3\ mol^{-1}$. Calculate the concentration of $COCl_2$ at equilibrium.

Solution

1. As in almost all these calculations, write the equation, leaving space above and below for initial and equilibrium conditions

	$CO\ (g)$	+ $Cl_2\ (g)$	$\rightleftharpoons COCl_2\ (g)$
Initial amount/mol			
Equilibrium amount/mol			

2. In this case it is convenient to work first in terms of initial and equilibrium amounts, and then divide them by the volume later when substituting concentrations into the equilibrium law. Indicate the initial amounts:

	$CO\ (g)$	+ $Cl_2\ (g)$	$\rightleftharpoons COCl_2\ (g)$
Initial amount/mol	0.20	0.10	0
Equilibrium amount/mol			

3. Calculate the amounts at equilibrium in terms of one unknown amount.
   a Let the amount of $COCl_2$ formed be x mol.
   b The balanced equation tells us that at equilibrium

$$\text{amount of CO} = \text{initial amount} - \text{amount reacted}$$
$$= (0.20 - x)\ \text{mol}$$

   c By similar reasoning, at equilibrium

$$\text{amount of } Cl_2 = (0.10 - x)\ \text{mol}$$

4. Put these equilibrium amounts in the appropriate spaces under the equation:

	$CO\ (g)$	$+\ Cl_2\ (g)$	$\rightleftharpoons COCl_2\ (g)$
Initial amount/mol	0.20	0.10	0
Equilibrium amount/mol	$(0.20 - x)$	$(0.10 - x)$	x

5. Write the equilibrium law in terms of concentrations:

$$K_c = \frac{[COCl_2\ (g)]}{[CO\ (g)]\,[Cl_2\ (g)]}$$

6. Put the equilibrium amounts in terms of concentrations by dividing by the volume; substitute these into the equilibrium law:

$$[COCl_2\ (g)] = \frac{x}{3.0}\ \text{mol dm}^{-3}$$

$$[CO\ (g)] = \frac{0.20 - x}{3.0}\ \text{mol dm}^{-3}$$

$$[Cl_2\ (g)] = \frac{0.10 - x}{3.0}\ \text{mol dm}^{-3}$$

$$0.410\ \text{dm}^3\ \text{mol}^{-1} = \frac{\frac{x}{3.0}\ \text{mol dm}^{-3}}{\frac{0.20 - x}{3.0}\ \text{mol dm}^{-3} \times \frac{0.10 - x}{3.0}\ \text{mol dm}^{-3}}$$

7. The equation becomes:

$$0.410 = \frac{\frac{x}{3.0}}{\frac{0.20 - x}{3.0} \times \frac{0.10 - x}{3.0}}$$

Simplify this equation:

$$0.410 = \frac{3x}{(0.20 - x)\times(0.10 - x)} = \frac{3x}{0.020 - 0.30x + x^2}$$

$$\text{or } 0.0082 - 0.123x + 0.410x^2 = 3x$$

Put this quadratic equation in the standard form

$$0.410x^2 - 3.123x + 0.0082 = 0$$

8. Solve this quadratic equation. The solutions of this equation are:

$$x = \frac{-b \pm \sqrt{b^2 - 4ac}}{2a}$$

for which $a = 0.410$, $b = -3.123$, $c = 0.0082$.

$$x = \frac{3.123 \pm \sqrt{(3.123)^2 - (4 \times 0.410 \times 0.0082)}}{(2 \times 0.410)}$$

$$= \frac{3.123 \pm \sqrt{9.7531 - 0.0134}}{0.820} = \frac{3.123 \pm \sqrt{9.7397}}{0.820} = \frac{3.123 \pm 3.121}{0.820}$$

$$\therefore x = 7.6 \text{ or } x = 2.4 \times 10^{-3}$$

Solving a quadratic equation produces two roots. Because the system began with 0.20 mol of CO and 0.10 mol of Cl_2, it is impossible to produce 7.6 mol of $COCl_2$. Therefore, the correct root is $x = 2.4 \times 10^{-3}$.

9. The amount of $COCl_2$ at equilibrium is 2.4×10^{-3} mol.

$$\text{Now, concentration} = \frac{\text{amount}}{\text{volume}}$$

$$\therefore [COCl_2 (g)] = \frac{2.4 \times 10^{-3} \text{ mol}}{3.0 \text{ dm}^3} = 8.0 \times 10^{-4} \text{ mol dm}^{-3}$$

Now try the following exercises, some of which require the solution of a quadratic equation.

EXERCISE 29

Answer on page 85

A

Carbon monoxide will react with steam under the appropriate conditions according to the following reversible reaction:

$$CO (g) + H_2O (g) \rightleftharpoons CO_2 (g) + H_2 (g); \quad \Delta H^{\circ} = -40 \text{ kJ mol}^{-1}$$

Calculate the number of moles of hydrogen in the equilibrium mixture when three moles of carbon monoxide and three moles of steam are placed in a reaction vessel of constant volume and maintained at a temperature at which the equilibrium constant has a numerical value of 4.00.

EXERCISE 30

Answers on page 85

For the equilibrium:

$$PCl_5 (g) \rightleftharpoons PCl_3 (g) + Cl_2 (g)$$

$K_c = 0.19$ mol dm^{-3} at 250°C. 2.085 g of PCl_5 was heated to 250°C in a sealed vessel of 500 cm^3 capacity and maintained at this temperature until equilibrium was established. Calculate the concentrations of PCl_5, PCl_3 and Cl_2 at equilibrium.

EXERCISE 31

Answer on page 86

For the reaction:

$$H_2 (g) + I_2 (g) \rightleftharpoons 2HI (g)$$

the equilibrium constant = 49.0 at 444°C. If 2.00 mol of hydrogen and 2.00 mol of iodine are heated in a closed vessel at 444°C until equilibrium is attained, calculate the composition in moles of the equilibrium mixture.

EXERCISE 32
Answer on page 86

For the equilibrium:

$$C_2H_5OH\ (l) + C_2H_5CO_2H\ (l) \rightleftharpoons C_2H_5CO_2C_2H_5\ (l) + H_2O\ (l)$$

propanoic acid ethyl propanoate

$K_c = 7.5$ at 50°C. If 50.0 g of C_2H_5OH is mixed with 50.0 g of $C_2H_5CO_2H$, what mass of ethyl propanoate will be formed at equilibrium?

For extra practice, or for revision, there are some further exercises of this type in Appendix 1.4 on page 67.

So far in this book we have expressed the equilibrium law only in terms of the equilibrium **concentrations** of reactants and products. However, for gaseous systems, it is often convenient to use partial pressures rather than concentrations. The equilibrium law still applies, but gives a different equilibrium constant, K_p, which we now consider.

CHAPTER 5

THE EQUILIBRIUM CONSTANT, K_p

For equilibrium involving gases, the equilibrium law can be expressed in terms of partial pressures because the partial pressure of each gas (i.e. its contribution to the total pressure) is proportional to its concentration. The equilibrium constant is then given the symbol K_p.

5.1 Writing an expression for K_p and calculating its value

OBJECTIVES

When you have finished this section you should be able to:

- write an expression for the **equilibrium constant, K_p**, for a gaseous system;
- calculate the value of K_p for a reaction given
  - **a** **partial pressures** at equilibrium,
  - **b** equilibrium amounts and total pressure.

Read the section of your textbook(s) which shows you how to write the equilibrium law in terms of partial pressures. If necessary, remind yourself of the definition of partial pressure and the relationship between partial pressure and **mole fraction**.

EXERCISE 33
Answers on page 87

Write an expression for K_p for each of the following equilibrium systems. Assume all pressures are measured in atmospheres (atm), and include units for K_p.

a $2NH_3\,(g) \rightleftharpoons N_2\,(g) + 3H_2\,(g)$,
b $2SO_2\,(g) + O_2\,(g) \rightleftharpoons 2SO_3\,(g)$,
c $C\,(s) + CO_2\,(g) \rightleftharpoons 2CO\,(g)$,
d $CaCO_3\,(s) \rightleftharpoons CaO\,(s) + CO_2\,(g)$,
e $NH_4HS\,(s) \rightleftharpoons NH_3\,(g) + H_2S\,(g)$.

To calculate K_p, we simply substitute equilibrium partial pressures into the equilibrium law expression. It is just like substituting equilibrium concentrations to calculate K_c. To see if you can do this, try the following exercise.

EXERCISE 34
Answer on page 87

In the equilibrium system

$$2SO_2\,(g) + O_2\,(g) \rightleftharpoons 2SO_3\,(g)$$

at 700 K, the partial pressures of the gases in an equilibrium mixture are:

$$p_{SO_2} = 0.090 \text{ atm}, p_{SO_3} = 4.5 \text{ atm}, p_{O_2} = 0.083 \text{ atm}.$$

Calculate K_p for this system.

There are some similar exercises, for more practice or for revision, in Appendix A1.5 on page 68.

In the next exercise, you have to calculate the partial pressures before substituting in the equilibrium law expression. Remember that

$$\text{partial pressure} = \text{mole fraction} \times \text{total pressure}$$

$$\text{mole fraction} = \frac{\text{amount of one component}}{\text{total amount of all components}}$$

EXERCISE 35
Answers on page 87

Analysis of the equilibrium system

$$N_2\,(g) + 3H_2\,(g) \rightleftharpoons 2NH_3\,(g)$$

showed 25.1 g of NH_3, 12.8 g of H_2 and 59.6 g of N_2.

a Calculate the mole fraction of each gas.
b The total pressure of the system was 10.0 atm. Calculate the partial pressure of each gas.
c Calculate K_p for the system.

The following exercises are similar.

EXERCISE 36
Answers on page 87

Phosphorus pentachloride dissociates on heating according to the equation:

$$PCl_5\,(g) \rightleftharpoons PCl_3\,(g) + Cl_2\,(g)$$

At a pressure of 10.0 atm and a temperature of 250°C the amount of each gas present at equilibrium was: 0.33 mol of PCl_5, 0.67 mol of PCl_3 and 0.67 mol of Cl_2. Calculate the value of K_p.

EXERCISE 37
Answers on page 88

Ammonium aminomethanoate, $NH_2CO_2NH_4$, decomposes according to the equation:

$$NH_2CO_2NH_4\,(s) \rightleftharpoons 2NH_3\,(g) + CO_2\,(g)$$

In a particular system at 293 K, there was 0.224 mol of CO_2 and 0.142 mol of NH_3 at a total pressure of 1.83 atm. Calculate K_p for this system.

If you had difficulty with the preceding exercises or you are revising the topic, try some more from Appendix A1.6 on page 68.

K_p and K_c generally have different values and units (look, for example, at Exercises 21 and 36), but the two quantities are related because partial pressure is proportional to concentration. Ask your teacher if your syllabus requires you to know this relationship; if so, turn to Appendix 2 on page 70.

Now that you can write an expression for K_p, we show you how to use it to consider the effect on a system of changing the total pressure.

5.2 The effect on an equilibrium system of changing pressure

In Part A you applied Le Chatelier's principle to determine the **direction** of any shift in equilibrium position caused by changing the total pressure. Now you can apply the equilibrium law to show why Le Chatelier's principle works in relation to pressure changes. You can also calculate the pressure change required to alter the equilibrium concentrations to a given extent.

OBJECTIVES

When you have finished this section you should be able to:

- show how the equilibrium law determines the effect on an equilibrium system of **changing the total pressure;**
- calculate the pressure change required to alter, to a given extent, the proportions of reactants and products in a particular equilibrium system.

We show you how to achieve these objectives by means of a Revealing Exercise, followed by a Worked Example, both of which concern the equilibrium system

$$2SO_2\,(g) + O_2\,(g) \rightleftharpoons 2SO_3\,(g)$$

EXERCISE
Revealing

Q1 Write the equilibrium law expression for the system $2SO_2\ (g) + O_2\ (g) \rightleftharpoons 2SO_3\ (g)$.

A1

$$K_p = \frac{p^2_{SO_3}}{p^2_{SO_2} \times p_{O_2}}$$

Q2 Write an expression for the partial pressure of each gas in terms of its mole fraction X and the total pressure p_T.

A2 $p_{SO_3} = X_{SO_3}p_T, \quad p_{SO_2} = X_{SO_2}p_T, \quad p_{O_2} = X_{O_2}p_T$

Q3 Substitute your answers to **Q2** into the equilibrium law expression for K_p and simplify the equation.

A3

$$K_p = \frac{(X_{SO_3}p_T)^2}{(X_{SO_2}p_T)^2 \times (X_{O_2}p_T)} = \frac{1}{p_T} \times \frac{X^2_{SO_3}}{X^2_{SO_2} \times X_{O_2}}$$

Q4 If the pressure of the system is doubled (at constant temperature), which mole fractions must increase and which must decrease? (The new values must give the same value of K_p as before.)

A4 The mole fraction of SO_3 must increase and the mole fractions of SO_2 and O_2 must decrease.

Q5 In which direction must the equilibrium position shift in order to change the mole fractions? Is this in accordance with Le Chatelier's principle?

A5 The equilibrium shifts to the right, as predicted by Le Chatelier's principle.

The same method could be applied to any gaseous equilibrium system. We now show you, in a Worked Example, how to use the expression you derived in **A3** of the Revealing Exercise.

WORKED EXAMPLE

At 1100 K, $K_p = 0.13\ \text{atm}^{-1}$ for the system

$$2SO_2\ (g) + O_2\ (g) \rightleftharpoons 2SO_3\ (g)$$

If 2.00 mol of SO_2 and 2.00 mol of O_2 are mixed and allowed to react, what must the total pressure be to give a 90% yield of SO_3?

Solution

1. Write the balanced equation, leaving room above and below to put in initial amounts and equilibrium amounts:

Initial amount/mol

$$2SO_2\ (g) + O_2\ (g) \rightleftharpoons 2SO_3\ (g)$$

Equilibrium amount/mol

2. Put in the initial amounts:

Initial amount/mol	2.00	2.00	0
	$2SO_2$ (g) +	O_2 (g) $\rightleftharpoons$	$2SO_3$ (g)
Equilibrium amount/mol			

3. Calculate the amounts at equilibrium:
   a The amount of SO_3 produced = 2.00 mol × (90/100) = 1.80 mol.
   b The amount of SO_2 left at equilibrium
   = initial amount – amount reacted
   = (2.00 – 1.80) mol = 0.20 mol.
   c Amount of oxygen reacting = ½ × amount of SO_2 reacting
   = ½ × 1.80 mol = 0.900 mol.
   The amount of oxygen remaining at equilibrium
   = initial amount – amount reacting
   = (2.00 – 0.900) mol = 1.10 mol.

4. Tabulate this equilibrium information.

Initial amount/mol	2.0	2.0	0
	$2SO_2$ (g) +	O_2 (g) $\rightleftharpoons$	$2SO_3$ (g)
Equilibrium amount/mol	0.20	1.10	1.80

5. Write an expression for the partial pressure of each gas. The total amount of gas present = (0.20 + 1.10 + 1.80) mol = 3.10 mol

$$p_{SO_3} = X_{SO_3} p_T = \frac{1.80}{3.10} \times p_T$$

Similarly for the other two partial pressures:

$$p_{SO_2} = \frac{0.20}{3.10} \times p_T; \quad p_{O_2} = \frac{1.10}{3.10} \times p_T$$

6. Write an expression for K_p and substitute the partial pressures:

$$K_p = \frac{p^2_{SO_3}}{p^2_{SO_2} \times p_{O_2}}$$

$$\therefore\ 0.13\ \text{atm}^{-1} = \frac{\left(\frac{1.80}{3.10}\right)^2 p_T^2}{\left(\frac{0.20}{3.10}\right)^2 p_T^2 \times \left(\frac{1.10}{3.10}\right) p_T}$$

7. Solve this equation for p_T:

$$\therefore\ 0.13\ \text{atm}^{-1} = \frac{0.337}{0.00416 \times 0.355 p_T}$$

$$p_T = \frac{0.337}{0.13\ \text{atm}^{-1} \times 0.00416 \times 0.355} = 1.76 \times 10^3\ \text{atm}$$

The pressure calculated in the worked example is far too high for economic production.

In the next exercise, you calculate the pressure required for a more modest conversion.

EXERCISE 38
Answer on page 88

For the system described in the worked example, calculate the pressure necessary for 20% conversion of the SO_2.

There are similar problems in Appendix A1.7 on page 69.

EXERCISE 39
Answer on page 88

Sulphur dioxide and oxygen in the ratio 2 moles : 1 mole were mixed at a constant temperature of 1110 K and a constant pressure of 9 atm in the presence of a catalyst. At equilibrium, one third of the sulphur dioxide had been converted into sulphur trioxide:

$$2SO_2\,(g) + O_2\,(g) \rightleftharpoons 2SO_3\,(g)$$

Calculate the equilibrium constant (K_p) for this reaction under these conditions.

You have seen how the equilibrium yield of SO_3 varies with temperature, with pressure, and with the ratio of SO_2 to O_2 in the initial mixture. In the industrial manufacture of sulphuric acid via SO_3 by the contact process, it is important not only to achieve a good equilibrium yield but also to maintain a high rate of production at reasonable cost. The conditions are chosen to achieve a balance between these conflicting requirements.

In the next exercise you use a different unit of pressure, which will be discussed in more detail in ILPAC Volume 9.

EXERCISE 40
Answer on page 89

A sample of dinitrogen tetroxide is 66% dissociated at a pressure of 98.3 kPa (747 mmHg) and a temperature of 60°C. (Standard pressure = 100 kPa (760 mmHg).) Calculate the value of K_p for the equilibrium at 60°C, stating the units.

When considering mixtures of gases, a useful concept is 'average molar mass'. We deal with this in the next section.

5.3 Average molar mass of a gaseous mixture

You might be asked to calculate the average molar mass of a mixture of gases from the amounts present or, alternatively, to calculate the relative amounts present from the average molar mass of a mixture.

OBJECTIVE

When you have finished this section you should be able to:
- calculate the **average molar mass** of a gaseous mixture.

We show you how to do this calculation in a Worked Example. You may like to try to solve the problem yourself before you look at our solution.

WORKED EXAMPLE

Calculate the average molar mass of a mixture which contains 0.20 mol of SO_2, 1.10 mol of O_2 and 1.80 mol of SO_3.

Solution

Each component of the mixture contributes to the average molar mass, $\overline{M}$, in proportion to its mole fraction, X.

$$\overline{M} = X_{SO_2} M_{SO_2} + X_{O_2} M_{O_2} + X_{SO_3} M_{SO_3}$$

$$= \frac{0.20}{3.10} \times 64.1\text{ g mol}^{-1} + \frac{1.10}{3.10} \times 32.0\text{ g mol}^{-1} + \frac{1.80}{3.10} \times 80.1\text{ g mol}^{-1}$$

$$= (4.1 + 11.4 + 46.5)\text{ g mol}^{-1} = \mathbf{62.0\ g\ mol^{-1}}$$

Now do the following exercises.

EXERCISE 41
Answers on page 89

$$2NO_2\,(g) \rightleftharpoons 2NO\,(g) + O_2\,(g).$$

For this system, a particular equilibrium mixture has the composition 0.96 mol of NO_2 (g), 0.040 mol of NO (g), 0.020 mol of O_2 (g) at 700 K and 0.20 atm.

a Calculate the equilibrium constant, K_p, for this reaction under the stated conditions.
b Calculate the average molar mass of the mixture under the stated conditions.

EXERCISE 42
Answers on page 90

0.20 mol of carbon dioxide was heated with excess carbon in a closed vessel until the following equilibrium was attained:

$$CO_2\,(g) + C\,(s) \rightleftharpoons 2CO\,(g)$$

It was found that the average molar mass of the gaseous equilibrium mixture was 36 g mol^{-1}.

a Calculate the mole fraction of carbon monoxide in the equilibrium gaseous mixture.
b The pressure at equilibrium in the vessel was 12 atm. Calculate K_p for the equilibrium at the temperature of the experiment.
c Calculate the mole fraction of carbon monoxide which would be present in the equilibrium mixture if the pressure were reduced to 2.0 atm at the same temperature.

There are some more problems on average molar mass in Appendix A1.8 on page 69.

Now we consider again the effect on an equilibrium system of changing temperature, this time in terms of the equilibrium law.

THE VARIATION OF EQUILIBRIUM CONSTANT WITH TEMPERATURE

You already know, from Part A, that the **direction** of a shift in equilibrium brought about by a temperature change is determined by the sign of the standard enthalpy change, ΔH°. You should not be surprised to find that the **extent** of the shift depends on the **value** of ΔH°.

OBJECTIVE

When you have finished this chapter you should be able to:

- describe how **equilibrium constants vary with temperature.**

Since a change in temperature does not, of itself, change the concentration of a substance, it follows that any shift in equilibrium position must be due to a change in the equilibrium constant. You explore this idea in the next exercise.

EXERCISE 43

Answers on page 90

a Write expressions for K_p for the following equilibrium systems:
i) $H_2\,(g) + I_2\,(g) \rightleftharpoons 2HI\,(g)$; $\Delta H^{\circ} = -9.6\ \text{kJ mol}^{-1}$,
ii) $N_2\,(g) + O_2\,(g) \rightleftharpoons 2NO\,(g)$; $\Delta H^{\circ} = +180\ \text{kJ mol}^{-1}$,
iii) $N_2\,(g) + 3H_2\,(g) \rightleftharpoons 2NH_3\,(g)$; $\Delta H^{\circ} = -92\ \text{kJ mol}^{-1}$.

b According to Le Chatelier's principle, which way does the equilibrium shift, in each case, with an increase in temperature?

c Use your answers for **a** and **b** to decide whether K_p increases or decreases with increasing temperature.

d Which equilibrium constant do you think might change most for a given change in temperature?

The effect on equilibrium of changing temperature is therefore different from the effects of changing concentration and pressure. Remember that:

equilibrium constants vary with temperature; they do not vary with pressure or concentrations;

if ΔH° is positive, K increases with temperature (more products);
if ΔH° is negative, K decreases with temperature (more reactants).

You also know, from ILPAC Volume 2 (Chemical Energetics), that the extent to which a reaction 'goes' depends on the value of the standard free energy change, ΔG°. You might therefore expect ΔG° and K to be related. Ask your teacher if your syllabus requires you to know the mathematical relationship between ΔG° and K; if it does, you should work through Appendix 2 on page 70.

Having considered some homogeneous equilibrium systems, we now apply the equilibrium law to an important group of heterogeneous systems – sparingly soluble salts in contact with their saturated solutions.

CHAPTER 7

SOLUBILITY PRODUCTS FOR SLIGHTLY SOLUBLE SALTS

Equilibria involving sparingly soluble salts deserve special attention because of their importance in chemical analysis. A simple application of the equilibrium law helps us to understand how precipitation can be controlled.

OBJECTIVES

When you have finished this chapter you should be able to:

- write an expression for the **solubility product** of a slightly soluble salt;
- calculate a solubility product from **solubility** data;
- calculate solubility from solubility product.

7.1 Writing an expression for solubility product

Find out from your textbook(s) how to apply the equilibrium law in order to write an expression for the solubility product, K_s, of a slightly soluble salt. We show you how to do the calculations after the next exercise.

EXERCISE 44
Answers on page 90

Write expressions for the solubility products, K_s, for the following systems; assume concentrations are measured in mol dm^{-3} and include the unit of K_s.

a $BaSO_4\ (s) \rightleftharpoons Ba^{2+}\ (aq) + SO_4^{2-}\ (aq)$

b $CaF_2\ (s) \rightleftharpoons Ca^{2+}\ (aq) + 2F^-\ (aq)$

c $Ag_3PO_4\ (s) \rightleftharpoons 3Ag^+\ (aq) + PO_4^{3-}\ (aq)$

In Experiment 3, page 50, you determine the solubility product of calcium hydroxide by titration. You need about 10–15 minutes to prepare the solutions (Procedure steps 1 and 2) now, or at least 24 hours before you do the titration. The next section will help you to do the calculation at the end of the experiment.

7.2 Calculating solubility product from solubility

We show you how to do this type of calculation by means of Worked Example.

WORKED EXAMPLE

The solubility of silver sulphide, Ag_2S, is 2.48×10^{-15} mol dm^{-3}. Calculate its solubility product.

Solution

1. Write the equation representing the dissolving of silver sulphide, leaving space above and below the equation for initial and equilibrium concentrations:

Initial concn/mol dm^{-3}		0	0
	$Ag_2S\ (s) \rightleftharpoons$	$2Ag^+\ (aq)$ +	$S^{2-}\ (aq)$
Equilibrium concn/mol dm^{-3}			

2. Calculate the concentrations of sulphide ions and silver ions.
   The solubility indicates the amount of silver sulphide in a saturated solution. The balanced equation shows that every mole of Ag_2S which dissolves produces one mole of S^{2-} and two moles of Ag^+. Hence, at this temperature, in a saturated solution of Ag_2S

$$[S^{2-}\ (aq)] = 2.48 \times 10^{-15}\ \text{mol dm}^{-3}$$

and

$$[Ag^+ (aq)] = 2 \times 2.48 \times 10^{-15} \text{ mol dm}^{-3} = 4.96 \times 10^{-15} \text{ mol dm}^{-3}$$

Put these values below the equation:

Initial concn/mol dm^{-3}			0		0
	Ag_2S (s)	$\rightleftharpoons$	$2Ag^+$ (aq)	+	S^{2-} (aq)
Equilibrium concn/mol dm^{-3}			4.96×10^{-15}		2.48×10^{-15}

3. Write the expression for K_s, substitute the equilibrium concentrations and do the arithmetic.
   $K_s = [Ag^+ (aq)]^2[S^{2-} (aq)]$
   $= (4.96 \times 10^{-15} \text{ mol dm}^{-3})^2 \times (2.48 \times 10^{-15} \text{ mol dm}^{-3})$
   $= \mathbf{6.10 \times 10^{-44} \text{ mol}^3 \text{ dm}^{-9}}$

In this type of calculation some students wonder why a concentration term is both doubled and squared. The explanation is as follows: firstly, the stoichiometry tells us that $[Ag^+ (aq)]$ is twice the solubility; secondly, the form of the equilibrium law tells us that the silver ion concentration is squared.

Now try the following exercise.

EXERCISE 45

Answers on page 91

Calculate the solubility products of the following substances from their solubilities.

	Substances	**Solubility/mol dm^{-3}**
a	$CdCO_3$	1.58×10^{-7}
b	CaF_2	2.15×10^{-4}
c	$Cr(OH)_3$	1.39×10^{-8}

Now you can complete Experiment 3, provided that 24 hours have elapsed since you made up the solutions. Your teacher may wish to use it to assess your practical skills.

EXPERIMENT 3 Determining a solubility product

Aim The purpose of this experiment is to determine the solubility and solubility product of calcium hydroxide.

Introduction

The equilibrium between solid calcium hydroxide and its ions in an aqueous solution is

$$Ca(OH)_2\,(s) \rightleftharpoons Ca^{2+}\,(aq) + 2OH^-\,(aq)$$

The concentration of hydroxide ions can be determined by titration with hydrochloric acid; the concentration of calcium ions can be calculated from the titration result.

Requirements

- safety spectacles
- 4 stoppered bottles, 250 cm^3
- labels for bottles
- spatula
- calcium hydroxide, solid, $Ca(OH)_2$
- measuring cylinder, 100 cm^3
- distilled water
- 4 filter funnels, **dry,** with filter papers
- 4 conical flasks, 250 cm^3
- thermometer 0–100°C (±1°C)
- pipette, 25 cm^3, and safety filler
- burette and stand, white tile
- small funnel
- hydrochloric acid solution, 0.1 M – standardised
- phenolphthalein indicator solution

Procedure

1. Into each of four bottles put about 2 g of powdered calcium hydroxide and about 100 cm^3 of distilled water. Stopper securely.
2. Shake well for about a minute. Label each bottle with your name, experiment and date, and set aside for a day or more.
3. Rinse and fill the burette with standardised hydrochloric acid.
4. Filter the contents of one bottle, allowing the first 5 cm^3 to run to waste and collecting the rest in a dry conical flask. (The first few cm^3 are rejected because they are less concentrated in solute than the rest. The filter paper adsorbs solute until it attains equilibrium with the solution. Yet another equilibrium!)

To minimise absorption of carbon dioxide, steps 5 and 6 should be done quickly (with due care!) and with only the minimum shaking that will ensure mixing.

5. Rinse the pipette with the calcium hydroxide solution and transfer 25.0 cm^3 to a conical flask (this need not be dry).
6. Add two drops of phenolphthalein to the flask and titrate the solution until the pink colour just disappears. Record your burette readings in a copy of Results Table 5.
7. Repeat steps 4, 5 and 6 for the other three solutions.
8. Record the temperature.

Results Table 5

Solution in flask				mol dm^{-3}		cm^3
Solution in burette				mol dm^{-3}		
Indicator						
		Trial	1	2	3	4
Burette readings	Final					
	Initial					
Volume used/cm^3						
Mean titre/cm^3						

Calculation

1. Calculate the concentration of hydroxide ions in a saturated solution of calcium hydroxide.
2. From the equilibrium concentration of hydroxide ions calculate the equilibrium concentration of calcium ions.
3. Calculate the solubility of calcium hydroxide at the temperature of your experiment. Compare your result with the value listed in your data book.
4. Calculate the solubility product from:
   a your result,
   b the solubility of calcium hydroxide given in your data book.

Since this experiment may be used as a practical assessment exercise, specimen results are not provided, but, if necessary, they may be available from your teacher.

Now that you know how to calculate solubility product from solubility, we show you how to do the reverse process.

7.3 Calculating solubility from solubility product

WORKED EXAMPLE

Calculate the solubility, in mol dm^{-3}, of calcium sulphate. K_s for calcium sulphate = 8.64×10^{-8} mol^2 dm^{-6}.

Solution

1. Write the equation for the solution of the salt, leaving room above and below for concentrations. Initially there is no Ca^{2+} (aq) or SO_4^{2-} (aq).

Initial concn/mol dm^{-3}		0	0
	$CaSO_4$ (s) $\rightleftharpoons$	Ca^{2+} (aq) +	SO_4^{2-} (aq)
Equilibrium concn/mol dm^{-3}			

2. From the balanced equation we know that the equilibrium concentration of Ca^{2+} (aq) is equal to that of SO_4^{2-} (aq). Let this be x mol dm^{-3}.

Initial concn/mol dm^{-3}		0	0
	$CaSO_4$ (s) $\rightleftharpoons$	Ca^{2+} (aq) +	SO_4^{2-} (aq)
Equilibrium concn/mol dm^{-3}		x	x

3. Write the expression for K_s

$$K_s = [Ca^{2+} (aq)][SO_4^{2-} (aq)]$$

4. Substitute K_s and the equilibrium concentrations.

$$8.64 \times 10^{-8} \text{ mol}^2 \text{ dm}^{-6} = x \text{ mol dm}^{-3} \times x \text{ mol dm}^{-3}$$
$$x^2 = 8.64 \times 10^{-8}$$
$$x = 2.94 \times 10^{-4}$$
$$\therefore \text{ solubility} = \mathbf{2.94 \times 10^{-4} \text{ mol dm}^{-3}}$$

Try the next exercise, using a similar method.

EXERCISE 46
Answers on page 91

Calculate the solubilities of the following slightly soluble substances from their solubility products.

	Substance	Solubility product
a	CuS	6.3×10^{-36} mol^2 dm^{-6}
b	$Fe(OH)_2$	6.0×10^{-15} mol^3 dm^{-9}
c	Ag_3PO_4	1.25×10^{-20} mol^4 dm^{-12}.

7.4 Limitations of solubility product theory

Some data books do not list a value for the solubility product of calcium hydroxide, and none lists values for more soluble salts such as sodium chloride. The idea of solubility product strictly applies only to slightly soluble electrolytes, i.e. solutions in which the concentration of ions is very low. Usually the total ion concentration is not more than 0.01 mol dm^{-3}.

At higher concentrations, the ions interact with one another so that their effective concentrations differ from their actual concentrations. In this respect, very dilute solutions may be regarded as 'ideal solutions' which obey simple laws, just as gases at low pressure observe the ideal gas law

Calcium hydroxide is a border-line case; strictly, it is too soluble for its solution to be regarded as ideal, but the error is small enough for us to use calcium hydroxide as an example in a simple experiment. Obviously, titration would not be a good method for determining solubility products for less soluble salts; other methods are available, such as potentiometric or conductimetric measurements, which are beyond the scope of any current A-level syllabus.

So far in this chapter we have considered only pure solutions. Now we deal with mixtures of solutions with a common ion.

7.5 The common ion effect

OBJECTIVES

When you have finished this section you should be able to:

- perform calculations involving **solubility product** and the **common ion** effect;
- predict whether **precipitation** will occur given a solubility product and the concentrations of the solutions to be mixed.

We illustrate the common ion effect by a short experiment involving a fairly soluble salt. We then return to sparingly soluble salts for calculations. The next exercise is a useful introduction to the experiment.

EXERCISE 47
Answers on page 92

You are given a saturated solution of sodium chloride.

$$NaCl(s) \rightleftharpoons Na^+(aq) + Cl^-(aq)$$

According to Le Chatelier's principle, what do you expect to happen when

a the sodium ion concentration is increased,
b the chloride ion concentration is increased?

Now test your predictions by doing Experiment 4. It will take you no more than 10 minutes.

EXPERIMENT 4 Illustrating the common ion effect

Aim The purpose of this experiment is to demonstrate an example of the application of Le Chatelier's principle.

Introduction Although sodium chloride is quite soluble, we can use it to demonstrate the common ion effect. In the preceding exercise, you made some predictions based on Le Chatelier's principle; now you test them.

Requirements

- safety spectacles
- 2 test-tubes with corks, in a rack
- sodium chloride solution, saturated, NaCl
- hydrochloric acid, concentrated, HCl
- teat-pipette
- sodium hydroxide, pellets, NaOH
- spatula or forceps

Procedure

1. Carefully pour about 10 cm^3 of saturated sodium chloride solution into each of two test-tubes. Do not transfer any solid.
2. To the first test-tube carefully add four to five drops of concentrated hydrochloric acid. Cork the tube, shake gently and set aside.
3. To the second test-tube add one pellet of sodium hydroxide. **Use forceps or spatula to handle the sodium hydroxide**. Cork the tube, shake gently and set aside.
4. Note any observations.

HAZARD WARNING

Concentrated hydrochloric acid is a corrosive liquid and its vapour is harmful to the eyes, lungs and skin. Sodium hydroxide is corrosive. Therefore you **must**:

- wear safety spectacles;
- keep the stoppers on the bottles as much as possible.

Questions

Answers on page 92

1. What did you see happen in each test-tube?
2. Does this confirm your prediction in Exercise 47?
3. In the saturated solution of sodium chloride, what is the concentration of each ion? (Use your data book.)
4. The concentration of concentrated hydrochloric acid is approximately 12 mol dm^{-3}. Explain what happened to the sodium ions in solution when the hydrochloric acid was added.
5. Explain what happened to the chloride ions in solution when the sodium hydroxide pellet was added.
6. Why is no solubility product value given for sodium chloride in any data book?

Experiment 4 showed you how increasing the concentration of one of the ions in a saturated solution reduces the concentration of the other ion by causing precipitation. This is known as the **common ion effect**; read about it further in your textbook(s). Look for examples of calculations which help you to understand our worked example and the following exercises.

WORKED EXAMPLE

Calculate the solubility of silver chloride, AgCl, in

a pure water,
b 0.10 M NaCl.

$$K_s\,(\text{AgCl}) = 2.0 \times 10^{-10}\ \text{mol}^2\ \text{dm}^{-6}.$$

Solution

a This is not a new type of calculation but you need the result for comparison. Refer to the last worked example if necessary.

$$\text{Solubility of AgCl} = \sqrt{K_s} = \sqrt{2.0 \times 10^{-10}\ \text{mol}^2\ \text{dm}^{-6}}$$
$$= \mathbf{1.4 \times 10^{-5}\ mol\ dm^{-3}}$$

b i) Write the equation and indicate the concentrations present initially and at equilibrium.

Initial concn/mol dm^{-3}		0	0.10
	$AgCl(s) \rightleftharpoons$	$Ag^+(aq)$ +	$Cl^-(aq)$
Equilibrium concn/mol dm^{-3}		x	$(x + 0.10)$

If x mol dm^{-3} of AgCl dissolves, then x mol dm^{-3} of Ag^+ (aq) and x mol dm^{-3} of Cl^- (aq) are produced. The total concentration of chloride ions equals that produced by the AgCl dissolving plus the 0.10 mol dm^{-3} initially present.

ii) Write the equilibrium law expression

$$K_s = [\text{Ag}^+\,(\text{aq})]\,[\text{Cl}^-\,(\text{aq})]$$

iii) Substitute the equilibrium concentrations and the solubility product

$$2.0 \times 10^{-10}\,\text{mol}^2\ \text{dm}^{-6} = x \times (x + 0.10)\ \text{mol}^2\ \text{dm}^{-6}$$

iv) Now you can make a very useful approximation. In otherwise pure water the concentration of Ag^+ (aq) from dissolved AgCl is 1.4×10^{-5} mol dm^{-3}. Applying Le Chatelier's principle, addition of Cl^- will drive the equilibrium to the left thereby reducing the silver ion concentration still further. So you can assume that the concentration of chloride ions from the AgCl is negligible compared to the 0.10 mol dm^{-3} solution of Cl^- present initially. Expressed mathematically,

$$(x + 0.10) \text{ mol dm}^{-3} \approx 0.10 \text{ mol dm}^{-3}.$$

(You can test this approximation after the calculation.)

v) The equilibrium law expression now becomes

$$2.0 \times 10^{-10} = x \times 0.10$$

$$\therefore\ x = \frac{2.0 \times 10^{-10}}{0.10} = 2.0 \times 10^{-9}$$

vi) The solubility in 0.10 M NaCl = $[Ag^+ \text{(aq)}]$
$= x$ mol dm^{-3} = $\mathbf{2.0 \times 10^{-9}}$ **mol** $\mathbf{dm^{-3}}$

Note the dramatic effect of the common ion; this solubility is less than one thousandth of the solubility in water!

You can quite simply check that the approximation in step iv is valid:

$$x + 0.10 = (2.0 \times 10^{-9}) + 0.10 = 0.100000002 \approx 0.10$$

A better, but more tedious, check is to calculate x from the quadratic equation in step iii:

$$2.0 \times 10^{-10} = x \times (x + 0.10)$$

$$\therefore\ x^2 + 0.10x - 2.0 \times 10^{-10} = 0$$

$$\therefore\ x = \frac{-0.10 \pm \sqrt{0.010 + 8.0 \times 10^{-10}}}{2} = 2.0 \times 10^{-9}$$

You will find it very useful to make such approximations because they often make calculations much simpler, as you can see in the following exercises.

EXERCISE 48
Answers on page 92

At 20°C, the solubility product of strontium sulphate is 4.0×10^{-7} mol^2 dm^{-6}, and that of magnesium fluoride is 7.2×10^{-9} mol^3 dm^{-9}. Estimate, to two significant figures, the solubility at 20°C in mol dm^{-3} of

a strontium sulphate in a 0.1 M solution of sodium sulphate;
b magnesium fluoride in a 0.2 M solution of sodium fluoride.

EXERCISE 49
Answers on page 93

A saturated solution of strontium carbonate was filtered. When 50 cm^3 of the filtrate was added to 50 cm^3 of 1.0 M sodium carbonate solution, some strontium carbonate was precipitated. Calculate the concentration of strontium ions remaining in the solution. All the work was done at 25°C.

We now come to the last application of the solubility product principle that we cover in this book.

7.6 Will precipitation occur?

To predict whether precipitation will occur when solutions are mixed, you need to recognise that solubility product is a value which the product of ion concentrations in solution **can never exceed** at equilibrium.

We show you how to apply this idea in a worked example.

WORKED EXAMPLE

If 50.0 cm^3 of 0.050 M $AgNO_3$ is mixed with 50.0 cm^3 of 0.010 M $KBrO_3$, will a precipitate of $AgBrO_3$ form? $K_s(AgBrO_3) = 6 \times 10^{-5}$ mol^2 dm^{-6}.

Solution

1. Work out what the concentrations of Ag^+ and BrO_3^- would be after mixing but before any reaction:

   a Amount of $Ag^+ = 0.050\ dm^3 \times 0.050\ mol\ dm^{-3}$

$$[Ag^+ (aq)] = \frac{0.050\ dm^3 \times 0.050\ mol\ dm^{-3}}{0.100\ dm^3} = 0.025\ mol\ dm^{-3}$$

   (The volume is doubled, so the concentration is halved.)

   b Similarly, $[BrO_3^- (aq)] = \frac{1}{2} \times 0.010\ mol\ dm^{-3} = 0.0050\ mol\ dm^{-3}$.

2. Calculate the product of the ion concentrations (called the ion product).

   Ion product $= [Ag^+ (aq)][BrO_3^- (aq)]$

   $= 0.025\ mol\ dm^{-3} \times 0.0050\ mol\ dm^{-3} = 1.25 \times 10^{-4}\ mol^2\ dm^{-6}$.

3. Compare the value of the ion product with the solubility product.

   If the ion product is greater than K_s, precipitation will occur.
   If the ion product is less than K_s, precipitation will not occur.

   ∴ a **silver bromate precipitate** will appear because the ion product is greater than the solubility product.

To make sure that you can do this kind of problem, try the following two exercises.

EXERCISE 50
Answers on page 93

Will a precipitate of BaF_2 form if 150 cm^3 of 0.1 M $Ba(NO_3)_2$ is mixed with 50.0 cm^3 of 0.05 M KF? $K_s = 1.7 \times 10^{-6}$ mol^3 dm^{-9}.

EXERCISE 51
Answers on page 93

You are given the following **numerical values** only for the solubility products of various salts at 25°C.

K_s [silver chloride] $= 2 \times 10^{-10}$
K_s [lead(II) bromide] $= 3.9 \times 10^{-5}$
K_s [silver bromate(V)] $= 6.0 \times 10^{-5}$
K_s [magnesium hydroxide] $= 2.0 \times 10^{-11}$

a State the units for each of the above solubility products.

b Which of the following pairs of solutions (all of concentration 1.0×10^{-3} mol dm^{-3}) will form a precipitate when equal volumes are mixed at 25°C? Give reasons for your answers.

i) Silver nitrate and sodium chloride.
ii) Lead(II) nitrate and sodium bromide.
iii) Silver nitrate and potassium bromate(V).
iv) Magnesium sulphate and sodium hydroxide.

We now deal with the last application of the equilibrium law in this volume, namely the distribution of a solute between two immiscible solvents.

CHAPTER 8

DISTRIBUTION EQUILIBRIUM

You looked briefly at an example of distribution equilibrium in Part A; it is illustrated again in Fig. 12. You now consider similar systems in more detail.

Figure 12

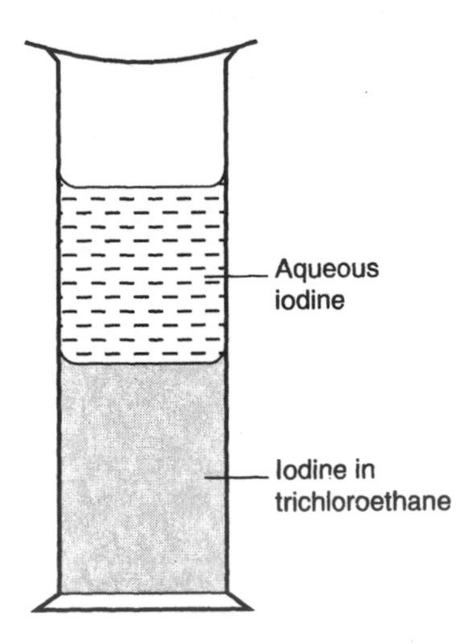

OBJECTIVES

When you have finished this chapter you should be able to:

- calculate the equilibrium constant, K_D, for a **distribution equilibrium** (the **distribution coefficient**), given the necessary data;
- apply the distribution equilibrium law to an **extraction** process.

Read about distribution equilibria in your textbook(s). Find out how to write expressions for distribution coefficients (sometimes called **partition coefficients**). You may find this application of the equilibrium law referred to as the **distribution law** or **partition law**.

Now you carry out an experiment to determine a distribution coefficient.

EXPERIMENT 5 Distribution equilibrium

Aim

The purpose of this experiment is to determine the value of the distribution coefficient for the equilibrium that exists when ammonia is distributed between water and an organic solvent, Volasil 244.

Introduction

In this experiment you shake some ammonia solution with Volasil 244 to establish equilibrium, and then determine the concentration of ammonia in each solvent by titration. This enables you to calculate the distribution coefficient, K_D

$$NH_3\,(Vol) \rightleftharpoons NH_3\,(aq) \quad (Vol = Volasil\ 244)$$

$$K_D = \frac{[NH_3\ (aq)]}{[NH_3\ (Vol)]}$$

Requirements

- safety spectacles
- measuring cylinder, 50 cm^3
- ammonia solution, 1.0 M NH_3
- Volasil 244 (**warning:** this liquid is flammable)
- separating funnel, 150 cm^3
- 2 beakers, 100 cm^3
- pipette, 10 cm^3, and safety filler
- 2 conical flasks, 150 cm^3
- wash-bottle of distilled water
- methyl orange indicator solution
- white tile
- burette, 50 cm^3, and stand
- hydrochloric acid, 0.010 M HCl (standardised)
- hydrochloric acid, 0.50 M HCl (standardised)

HAZARD WARNING

Volasil 244 is flammable. Therefore you **must**:

- Keep the stopper on the bottle as much as possible.
- Keep the liquid away from a naked flame.

Procedure

1. Pour about 50 cm^3 of ammonia solution into a separating funnel.
2. Pour about 50 cm^3 of Volasil 244 into the same separating funnel.
3. Holding the tap firmly in position with one hand and the stopper with the other, shake the separating funnel vigorously for about 10 seconds. Release the pressure inside by loosening the stopper for a moment.
4. Continue shaking for about half a minute, releasing the pressure every 10 seconds. Set aside until two layers separate.
5. Transfer the lower aqueous layer to a beaker. Rinse the pipette thoroughly, transfer 10.0 cm^3 to a flask, add about 20 cm^3 of water and a few drops of indicator solution, and titrate to the end-point with 0.50 M HCl.
6. Titrate two more 10 cm^3 samples and complete a copy of Results Table 6.
7. Transfer the organic layer to a beaker. Using a **dry** pipette, transfer 10.0 cm^3 to a conical flask. Add about 20 cm^3 of distilled water, a few drops of indicator and titrate the mixture with 0.010 M HCl until the yellow solution just changes to red and remains red after shaking. (It may take a few moments for all the ammonia to transfer from the organic layer and react with the acid.)
8. Titrate two more 10 cm^3 samples and complete a copy of Results Table 7.

Results Table 6

Solution in flask					mol dm^{-3}	cm^3
Solution in burette					mol dm^{-3}	
Indicator						
		Trial	1	2	3	4
Burette readings	Final					
	Initial					
Volume used/cm^3						
Mean titre/cm^3						

Results Table 7

Solution in flask					mol dm^{-3}	cm^3
Solution in burette					mol dm^{-3}	
Indicator						
		Trial	1	2	3	4
Burette readings	Final					
	Initial					
Volume used/cm^3						
Mean titre/cm^3						

Calculation

Specimen results and calculations are in the Teacher's Notes

1. Calculate the average concentration of ammonia in the aqueous layer from Results Table 6.
2. Calculate the average concentration of ammonia in the organic layer from Results Table 7.
3. Calculate the distribution coefficient.

$$K_D = \frac{[NH_3\ (aq)]}{[NH_3\ (Vol)]}$$

4. Compare your results with others in the class.

The calculation in the next exercise is similar to the calculation in Experiment 5; or you may choose to use a graphical method.

EXERCISE 52

Answer on page 94

Calculate the value of the distribution coefficient for the distribution equilibrium of butanedioic acid between water and ether from the following data. All experiments were performed at the same temperature.

Concn of acid in water /mol dm^{-3}	0.0759	0.108	0.158	0.300
Concn of acid in ether /mol dm^{-3}	0.0114	0.0162	0.0237	0.0451

The distribution of solute between two solvents is sometimes used in extraction and purification procedures. For instance, you could remove most of the ammonia from a solution in Volasil 244 by shaking it with water in several portions, as you discover in the next exercise.

These next two exercises involve the use of solvents which were widely used up to January 1995, but because they are now known to be ozone-damaging chemicals, they are no longer available.

EXERCISE 53

Answers on page 95

This exercise concerns the removal of ammonia from a solution in 1,1,1-trichloroethane (0.10 mol dm^{-3}) by shaking with water. $K_D = 290$.

How much ammonia remains in the organic layer after shaking 100 cm^3 of the solution with

a 100 cm^3 of water,
b four successive 25 cm^3 portions of water?

In the distribution equilibria you have considered so far, the solute is in the same molecular form in both solvents. For example, ammonia in 1,1,1-trichloroethane exists entirely as molecules of NH_3, and in water almost entirely as molecules of NH_3. There is a slight reaction in water:

$$NH_3\,(aq) + H_2O\,(l) \rightleftharpoons NH_4^+\,(aq) + OH^-\,(aq)$$

but K_c for this is about 10^{-7}, so virtually all the ammonia remains as molecules.

By contrast, ethanoic acid exists in aqueous solution almost entirely as CH_3CO_2H molecules and in 1,1,1-trichloroethane almost entirely as $(CH_3CO_2H)_2$ molecules, i.e. as dimers. You need not concern yourself with the derivation of the expression for K_D, but the simple result is that a squared term appears:

$$K_D = \frac{[CH_3CO_2H\,(tce)]}{[CH_3CO_2H\,(aq)]^2}$$

The next exercise concerns a similar equilibrium system.

EXERCISE 54

Answers on page 96

Trichloromethane was added to a series of aqueous solutions of ethanoic acid (acetic acid) and the mixtures were shaken at laboratory temperature. By titration the following concentrations of ethanoic acid were found in the two layers:

Trichloromethane/g dm^{-3}	17.5	43.5	84.6
Water/g dm^{-3}	292	479	642

By neglecting any dissociation of ethanoic acid in water, deduce its molecular formula in trichloromethane.

You may use graph paper if you wish.

End-of-unit test

To find out how well you have learned the material in this book, try the following End-of-unit test. Read the notes below before starting.

1. You should spend about 90 minutes on this test.
2. Hand your answers to your teacher for marking.

Questions 1–7 each contain statements followed by five suggested answers. Select the best answer in each case.

1. The reaction $CaCO_3$ (s) $\rightleftharpoons$ CaO (s) + CO_2 (g) is in equilibrium at 900°C and a partial pressure of carbon dioxide of 1×10^5 Pa. It could be confirmed that this equilibrium is dynamic by
   A Adding CaO and showing that the partial pressure of CO_2 falls.
   B Adding ^{14}C-labelled CO_2 until the partial pressure is 2×10^5 Pa and showing that the proportion of ^{14}C in the $CaCO_3$ increases.
   C Adding ^{14}C-labelled $CaCO_3$ while keeping the pressure at 1×10^5 Pa and showing that the proportion of ^{14}C in the CO_2 increases.
   D Increasing the partial pressure of CO_2 to 2×10^5 Pa and showing that the mass of $CaCO_3$ increases.
   E Absorbing the CO_2 in soda-lime and showing that all of the $CaCO_3$ is eventually decomposed. (1)

2. At a certain temperature, the equilibrium constant for the reaction:

$$CH_3CO_2H\ (l) + C_2H_5OH\ (l) \rightleftharpoons CH_3CO_2C_2H_5\ (l) + H_2O\ (l)$$

is 4. If one mole of ethanoic acid (CH_3CO_2H) is added to one mole of ethanol and the mixture is allowed to reach equilibrium, how many moles of ethanoic acid will be present in the equilibrium mixture?
   A 3/4,
   B 2/3,
   C 1/2,
   D 1/3,
   E 1/4. (1)

Questions 3–6 concern the effect on the equilibrium constant and the yield of product(s) of changes made to an equilibrium system.

	Effect on equilibrium constant	**Effect on yield of products**
A	increases	increases
B	decreases	decreases
C	no change	decreases
D	no change	increases
E	no change	no change

Select, from A to E, the effect produced when the following change is made to the equilibrium shown.

3. The pressure is increased on the equilibrium system

$$2SO_2\ (g) + O_2\ (g) \rightleftharpoons 2SO_3\ (g);\quad \Delta H^\circ = -196\ \text{kJ mol}^{-1}$$ (1)

4. A catalyst is added to the equilibrium system

$$2SO_2\ (g) + O_2\ (g) \rightleftharpoons 2SO_3\ (g);\quad \Delta H^\circ = -196\ \text{kJ mol}^{-1}$$ (1)

5. The temperature is increased for the equilibrium system

$$N_2 (g) + 3H_2 (g) \rightleftharpoons 2NH_3 (g); \quad \Delta H^\ominus = -92.4 \text{ kJ mol}^{-1}$$ (1)

6. Hydrogen is added to the equilibrium system

$$H_2 (g) + I_2 (g) \rightleftharpoons 2HI (g); \quad \Delta H^\ominus = +51.8 \text{ kJ mol}^{-1}$$ (1)

7. Twenty-five g of a solid X were dissolved in 100 g of water. The solution was shaken with 20 cm^3 of tetrachloromethane, and, when equilibrium was attained, 10 g of X were found to be dissolved in the tetrachloromethane. The molecular state of X was the same in both solvents. What is the value of the partition coefficient, $[X]_{CCl_4}/[X]_{H_2O}$?
A 0.67,
B 1.5,
C 2.5,
D 3.33,
E 7.5. (1)

In questions 8 and 9, one or more of the suggested responses is correct. Answer as follows:
A if **1, 2** and **3** are all correct,
B if **1** and **2** only are correct,
C if **2** and **3** only are correct,
D if **1** only is correct,
E if **3** only is correct.

Directions summarised				
A	B	C	D	E
1, 2, 3	**1, 2**	**2, 3**	**1**	**3**
correct	only	only	only	only

8. If a solution which is 0.0001 M with respect to carbonate ions, CO_3^{2-}, is mixed with an equal volume of a 0.0001 M solution of ions of a Group II metal, which of the following carbonates would be precipitated?

K_s (298 K)/mol^2 dm^{-6}
1 $MgCO_3$, 1.1×10^{-5}
2 $CaCO_3$, 5.0×10^{-9}
3 $SrCO_3$, 1.1×10^{-10}. (1)

9. The reaction between carbon dioxide and hydrogen to give steam and carbon monoxide is represented by the equation:

$$H_2 (g) + CO_2 (g) \rightleftharpoons H_2O (g) + CO (g); \quad \Delta H^\ominus = +41 \text{ kJ mol}^{-1}$$

Which of the following changes will increase the proportion of hydrogen in the equilibrium mixture?
1 Lowering the temperature of the system.
2 Increasing the pressure of the system.
3 Adding a catalyst. (1)

10. The equation for the reaction of ethanol and ethanoic acid is given below:

$$CH_3CO_2H\ (l) + C_2H_5OH\ (l) \rightleftharpoons CH_3CO_2C_2H_5\ (l) + H_2O\ (l)$$

3.0 g of ethanoic acid and 2.3 g of ethanol were equilibrated at 100°C for about one hour and then quickly cooled in an ice-bath. 50 cm^3 of aqueous sodium hydroxide of concentration 1.0 mol dm^{-3} were then added and the mixture titrated with hydrochloric acid of the same concentration. 33.3 cm^3 of acid were required.

a What is the meaning of the term 'equilibrate'? Why is the equilibrium mixture cooled rapidly in an ice-bath? (2)

b State Le Chatelier's principle and predict the effect of adding ethanol to the equilibrium mixture. (3)

c Give an expression for K_c and calculate its value using the data provided. (11)

d What would be the effect on the reaction of adding hydrogen ions as a catalyst? (2)

11. The equilibrium constant K_p for the reaction

$$PCl_5\ (g) \rightleftharpoons PCl_3\ (g) + Cl_2\ (g)$$

is 1.06×10^6 N m^{-2} at 250°C.

A sample of PCl_3 at an initial pressure of 1.01×10^6 N m^{-2} dissociates in the vapour phase at 250°C in a vessel of fixed volume.

i) Calculate the partial pressure of each species present at equilibrium and the final total pressure. (7)

ii) Will the same partial pressures be obtained if equal amounts (i.e. equal numbers of moles) of PCl_3 and Cl_2 are mixed at 250°C and the **final** pressure is the same as in part i)? Explain your reasoning. (2)

[The solution to a quadratic equation of the general form $ax^2 + bx + c = 0$ is $x = \{-b \pm \sqrt{(b^2 - 4ac)}\}/2a$].

12. **a** Write an expression for the solubility product of lead(II) chloride. (1)

b The solubility product of lead(II) chloride is 1.6×10^{-5} mol^3 dm^{-9} at a given temperature.

i) What is the solubility in mol dm^{-3} of lead(II) chloride in water at the same temperature?

ii) How many moles of chloride ion must be added to a 1.0 M solution of lead(II) nitrate at the same temperature in order just to cause a precipitate of lead(II) chloride? Assume that no change in volume occurs on adding the chloride ion. (4)

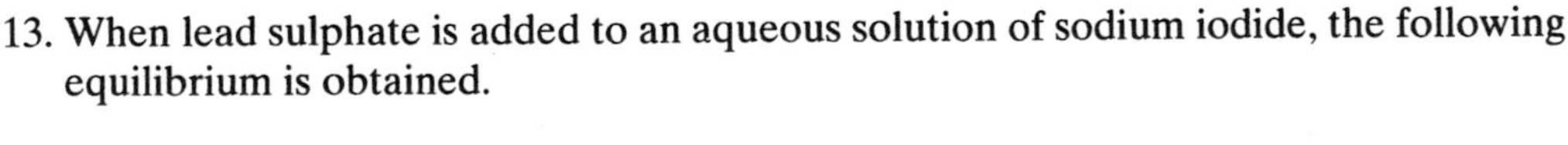

13. When lead sulphate is added to an aqueous solution of sodium iodide, the following equilibrium is obtained.

$$PbSO_4\ (s) + 2I^-\ (aq) \rightleftharpoons PbI_2\ (s) + SO_4^{2-}\ (aq)$$

The equilibrium constant for this reaction may be determined by adding an excess of lead sulphate to a known volume of a standard solution of sodium iodide and allowing the mixture to equilibrate in a water-bath thermostatically controlled at the desired temperature. Cold water is then added to the reaction mixture to 'freeze' the equilibrium and the mixture is then titrated with standard silver nitrate solution. In a typical experiment using 50.0 cm^3 of 0.1 M sodium iodide, a titre of 31.0 cm^3 of 0.1 M silver nitrate was obtained.

a Give an expression for the equilibrium constant, K, of the reaction. (1)

b Why is it not necessary to know the mass of lead sulphate used in the experiment? (1)

c From the data given above, calculate

i) the concentration of iodide ions present initially,
ii) the concentration of iodide ions present at equilibrium,
iii) the concentration of iodide ions which have reacted,
iv) the concentration of sulphate ions formed,
v) a value for K. (7)

(Total: 50 marks)

ADDITIONAL EXERCISES

Answers to these exercises, together with abbreviated methods, are on pages 97–102.

A1.1 Calculating K_c

EXERCISE 55 At 250°C, equilibrium for the following system was established:

$$PCl_5\ (g) \rightleftharpoons PCl_3\ (g) + Cl_2\ (g)$$

Analysis of the mixture showed that

$$[PCl_3\ (g)] = 1.50 \times 10^{-2}\ mol\ dm^{-3},\ [Cl_2\ (g)] = 1.50 \times 10^{-2}\ mol\ dm^{-3}$$
$$\text{and } [PCl_5\ (g)] = 1.18\ mol\ dm^{-3}.$$

Calculate the value of K_c at this temperature.

EXERCISE 56 Analysis of the equilibrium system

$$2SO_2\ (g) + O_2\ (g) \rightleftharpoons 2SO_3\ (g)$$

showed that

$$[SO_2\ (g)] = 0.23\ mol\ dm^{-3},\ [O_2\ (g)] = 1.37\ mol\ dm^{-3}$$
$$[SO_3\ (g)] = 0.92\ mol\ dm^{-3}.$$

Calculate the value of K_c at this temperature.

EXERCISE 57 At 700 K, analysis of the system

$$N_2\ (g) + 3H_2\ (g) \rightleftharpoons 2NH_3\ (g)$$

showed that

$$[N_2\ (g)] = 13.6\ mol\ dm^{-3},\ [H_2\ (g)] = 1.0\ mol\ dm^{-3},\ [NH_3\ (g)] = 1.5\ mol\ dm^{-3}.$$

Calculate the value of K_c at this temperature.

A1.2 Calculating equilibrium concentrations

EXERCISE 58 In the following equilibrium:

$$H_2\ (g) + I_2\ (g) \rightleftharpoons 2HI\ (g)$$

$K_c = 54.1$, at a particular temperature. The equilibrium mixture was found to contain H_2 at a concentration of 0.48×10^{-3} mol dm^{-3} and HI at a concentration of 3.53×10^{-3} mol dm^{-3}.What is the equilibrium concentration of I_2?

EXERCISE 59 For the equilibrium

$$C_5H_{10}\ (l) + CH_3CO_2H\ (l) \rightleftharpoons CH_3CO_2C_5H_{11}\ (l)$$
(pentene) (ethanoic acid) (pentyl ethanoate)

$K_c = 540$ dm^3 mol^{-1} at a certain temperature. An equilibrium mixture at this temperature contains 5.66×10^{-3} mol dm^{-3} of pentene and 2.55×10^{-3} mol dm^{-3} of ethanoic acid. Calculate the concentration of pentyl ethanoate in the mixture.

EXERCISE 60 This question concerns the equilibrium system

$$CH_3CO_2H\ (l) + C_2H_5OH\ (l) \rightleftharpoons CH_3CO_2C_2H_5\ (l) + H_2O\ (l);\ K_c = 4.0 \text{ at } 25°C$$

In a particular experiment, 0.33 mol of CH_3CO_2H, 0.66 mol of $CH_3CO_2C_2H_5$ and 0.66 mol of H_2O are found to be present. What amount of C_2H_5OH is present?

A1.3 Calculating K_c from equilibrium amounts

EXERCISE 61 In the following equilibrium system:

$$H_2\ (g) + I_2\ (g) \rightleftharpoons 2HI\ (g)$$

20.57 mol of hydrogen and 5.22 mol of iodine were allowed to reach equilibrium at 450°C. At this point, the mixture contained 10.22 mol of hydrogen iodide. Calculate the value of K_c at this temperature.

EXERCISE 62 The equilibrium

$$N_2O_4\ (l) \rightleftharpoons 2NO_2\ (l)$$

was established in a solvent at 10°C starting with 0.1307 mol dm^{-3} of N_2O_4 ; the equilibrium mixture was found to contain 0.0014 mol dm^{-3} of NO_2. Calculate the value of K_c at this temperature.

EXERCISE 63 In the following equilibrium:

$$C_2H_5OH\ (l) + CH_3CO_2H\ (l) \rightleftharpoons CH_3CO_2C_2H_5\ (l) + H_2O\ (l)$$

2.0 mol of ethanol and 1.0 mol of ethanoic acid were allowed to react to equilibrium at 25°C. At equilibrium the mixture contained 0.845 mol of ethyl ethanoate and the total volume was 30 cm^3. Calculate the value of K_c at this temperature.

A1.4 Calculating equilibrium amounts from initial amounts

EXERCISE 64 In the following equilibrium:

$$CH_3CO_2H\ (l) + C_2H_5OH\ (l) \rightleftharpoons CH_3CO_2C_2H_5\ (l) + H_2O\ (l)$$

8.0 mol of ethanoic acid and 6.0 mol of ethanol were placed in a 2.00 dm^3 vessel. What is the equilibrium amount of water? K_c at this temperature = 4.5.

EXERCISE 65 In the following equilibrium:

$$2HI\ (g) \rightleftharpoons H_2\ (g) + I_2\ (g)$$

1.0 mol of I_2 and 2.0 mol of H_2 are allowed to react in a 1.0 dm^3 vessel at 440°C. What are the equilibrium concentrations of HI, H_2 and I_2 at this temperature, given that $K_c = 0.02$ at 440°C?

EXERCISE 66 4.0 g of phosphorus pentachloride is allowed to reach equilibrium at 250°C in a 750 cm^3 vessel. $K_c = 0.19$ mol dm^{-3} for the following reaction at 250°C

$$PCl_5\,(g) \rightleftharpoons PCl_3\,(g) + Cl_2\,(g)$$

Calculate the amount of phosphorus pentachloride at equilibrium.

A1.5 Calculating K_p from partial pressures

EXERCISE 67 In the equilibrium system:

$$N_2O_4\,(g) \rightleftharpoons 2NO_2\,(g)$$

at 55°C, the partial pressures of the gases are $p_{N_2O_4} = 0.33$ atm and $p_{NO_2} = 0.67$ atm. Calculate K_p for this system.

EXERCISE 68 In the following equilibrium system:

$$2SO_2\,(g) + O_2\,(g) \rightleftharpoons 2SO_3\,(g)$$

at a certain temperature, the partial pressures of the gases are $p_{SO_2} = 2.3$ atm, $p_{O_2} = 4.5$ atm, $p_{SO_3} = 2.3$ atm. Calculate K_p for this system.

EXERCISE 69 Consider the following reaction:

$$H_2\,(g) + I_2\,(g) \rightleftharpoons 2HI\,(g)$$

At a certain temperature, analysis of the equilibrium mixture of the gases yielded the following results. $p_{H_2} = 0.25$ atm, $p_{I_2} = 0.16$ atm, $p_{HI} = 0.40$ atm. Calculate K_p for this reaction at the same temperature.

A1.6 Calculating K_p from equilibrium amounts

EXERCISE 70 In the following reaction:

$$CO_2\,(g) + H_2\,(g) \rightleftharpoons CO\,(g) + H_2O\,(g)$$

at a temperature of 100°C and a pressure of 2.0 atm, the amounts of each gas present at equilibrium were 6.2×10^{-3} mol of CO, 6.2×10^{-3} mol of H_2O, 0.994 mol of CO_2 and 0.994 mol of H_2. Calculate the value of K_p.

EXERCISE 71 An equilibrium mixture contained 0.40 mol of I atoms and 0.60 mol of I_2 molecules. The total pressure was 1.0 atm. Calculate the value of K_p at this temperature.

$$I_2\,(g) \rightleftharpoons 2I\,(g)$$

EXERCISE 72 In the following reaction:

$$H_2\,(g) + I_2\,(g) \rightleftharpoons 2HI\,(g)$$

at a temperature of 485°C and a pressure of 2.00 atm, the amount of each gas present at equilibrium was 0.56 mol of H_2, 0.060 mol of I_2 and 1.27 mol of HI. Calculate K_p at this temperature.

A1.7 Calculating pressure from K_p and equilibrium amounts

EXERCISE 73 In the following reaction:

$$2NO_2\,(g) \rightleftharpoons 2NO\,(g) + O_2\,(g)$$

at a temperature of 700 K, the amount of each gas present at equilibrium is 0.96 mol of NO_2, 0.04 mol of NO, and 0.02 mol of O_2. If $K_p = 6.8 \times 10^{-6}$ atm what must the total pressure have been to achieve this particular equilibrium mixture?

EXERCISE 74 $K_p = 3.72$ atm at 1000 K for the system:

$$C\,(s) + H_2O\,(g) \rightleftharpoons CO\,(g) + H_2\,(g)$$

What pressure must be applied to obtain a mixture containing 2.0 mol of CO, 1.0 mol of H_2 and 4.0 mol of H_2O?

EXERCISE 75 At 1000 K, $K_p = 1.9$ atm for the system:

$$C\,(s) + CO_2\,(g) \rightleftharpoons 2CO\,(g)$$

What must the total pressure be to have an equilibrium mixture containing 0.013 mol of CO_2 and 0.024 mol of CO?

A1.8 Average molar mass

EXERCISE 76 For the equilibrium:

$$N_2\,(g) + 3H_2\,(g) \rightleftharpoons 2NH_3\,(g)$$

at a particular temperature and a total pressure of 2.0 atm, an equilibrium mixture has the composition of 1.0 mol NH_3, 3.6 mol H_2 and 13.5 mol N_2.

a Calculate the equilibrium constant, K_p, for this reaction under the stated conditions.
b Calculate the average molar mass of the mixture under the stated conditions.

EXERCISE 77 For the equilibrium:

$$PCl_5\,(g) \rightleftharpoons PCl_3\,(g) + Cl_2\,(g)$$

a particular equilibrium mixture contains 0.20 mol PCl_5, 0.010 mol PCl_3 and 3.8 mol Cl_2, at a particular temperature and a total pressure of 3.0 atm.

a Calculate the equilibrium constant, K_p, for this reaction under the stated conditions.
b Calculate the average molar mass of the mixture under the stated conditions.

EXERCISE 78 For the equilibrium:

$$N_2O_4\,(g) \rightleftharpoons 2NO_2\,(g)$$

1.00 mol of N_2O_4 was introduced into a vessel and allowed to attain equilibrium at 308 K. It was found that the average molar mass of the mixture was 72.4 g mol^{-1}.

a Calculate the mole fraction of NO_2 in the equilibrium mixture.
b The pressure at equilibrium was 1.00 atm. Calculate K_p for the system at the temperature of the experiment.
c Calculate the mole fraction of NO_2 which would be present in the equilibrium mixture if the pressure were increased to 6.00 atm at the same temperature.

APPENDIX 2

FURTHER WORK

This appendix contains some topics which are required only for certain syllabuses. The first is fairly simple, but we consider the rest to be rather advanced for A-level. We suggest you proceed only after discussion with your teacher.

OBJECTIVES

When you have finished this appendix you should be able to:

- **calculate K_p from K_c** for a gaseous reaction, and vice versa;
- write an expression which relates **equilibrium constant, standard free energy change and temperature**;
- sketch graphs showing **minimum free energy** at equilibrium for a range of values of ΔG°;
- derive an expression which relates **equilibrium constant, standard enthalpy change and temperature**;
- calculate ΔH° from a series of values of equilibrium constants at different temperatures;
- calculate K at one temperature from ΔH° and K at another temperature.

We suggest that you work through the material in this appendix first and then use your textbook(s) afterwards for consolidation.

A2.1 The relationship between K_p and K_c

You derive the relationship by means of a Revealing Exercise which concerns the equilibrium system:

$$N_2O_4\,(g) \rightleftharpoons 2NO_2\,(g)$$

EXERCISE
Revealing

Q1 Write expressions for the amounts of the two gases, n_{NO_2} and $n_{N_2O_4}$, in terms of $[NO_2\,(g)]$, $[N_2O_4\,(g)]$ and the total volume V.

A1 $n_{NO_2} = [NO_2\,(g)]\,V$, $n_{N_2O_4} = [N_2O_4\,(g)]\,V$.

Q2 Use the ideal gas law to relate the amounts, n_{NO_2} and $n_{N_2O_4}$, to partial pressures.

A2 $p_{NO_2}V = n_{NO_2}RT$, $p_{N_2O_4}V = n_{N_2O_4}RT$.

Q3 Combine **A1** and **A2** to write expressions for p_{NO_2} and $p_{N_2O_4}$ in terms of $[NO_2\,(g)]$ and $[N_2O_4\,(g)]$.

A3 $p_{NO_2} = [NO_2\,(g)]\,RT$, $p_{N_2O_4} = [N_2O_4\,(g)]\,RT$.

Q4 Write an expression for K_p and substitute partial pressures from **A3**.

A4 $K_p = \dfrac{p^2_{NO_2}}{p_{N_2O_4}} = \dfrac{[NO_2\,(g)]^2\,(RT)^2}{[N_2O_4\,(g)]\,RT}$

Q5 Use **A4** to write an expression for K_p in terms of K_c.

A5 $K_p = K_cRT$.

In general,

$$K_p = K_c(RT^{\Delta n})$$

where Δn = number of moles of gaseous products – number of moles of gaseous reactants.

Use this expression to do the following exercises. (Choose the value of R which has the most appropriate unit.)

EXERCISE 79
Answer on page 103

For the equilibrium system:

$$PCl_5\,(g) \rightleftharpoons PCl_3\,(g) + Cl_2\,(g)$$

$K_p = 0.811$ atm at 523 K. Calculate K_c at this temperature.

EXERCISE 80
Answer on page 103

In the equilibrium system:

$$N_2\,(g) + 3H_2\,(g) \rightleftharpoons 2NH_3\,(g)$$

$K_c = 2.0$ dm^6 mol^{-2} at 620 K. Calculate K_p at this temperature.

EXERCISE 81
Answer on page 103

For the system:

$$H_2\,(g) + I_2\,(g) \rightleftharpoons 2HI\,(g)$$

show that $K_p = K_c$ at any temperature.

Now we look at the relationship between equilibrium constant and standard free energy change.

A2.2 The relationship between K and ΔG°

In ILPAC Volume 2, Chemical Energetics, you learned that it is the standard free energy change, ΔG°, which determines whether a reaction can proceed, rather than the standard enthalpy change, ΔH°.

We were unable to explain fully at that stage why it is that although ΔG (not ΔG°) must be negative for a spontaneous change, reactions where ΔG° has a small **positive** value may proceed partially, towards an equilibrium position. The reason is that ΔG° and K are related mathematically by an equation, which we now introduce without derivation.

$$\Delta G^\circ = -RT \ln K \quad \text{or} \quad \Delta G^\circ = -2.30\,RT \log K$$

We use 'ln' to mean 'logarithm to the base e' and 'log' to mean 'logarithm to the base 10'.

Note that for reactions involving a change in the amount of gas present, K in the equation above must be K_p; in other cases we may use K_c.

The equation shows that

if ΔG° is zero, $\log K$ is zero and $K = 1$

if ΔG° is negative, $\log K$ is positive and $K > 1$

if ΔG° is positive, $\log K$ is negative and $K < 1$

$K = 1$ for a simple reaction when there are equal concentrations of reactants and products. If $K > 1$ the products are favoured and if $K < 1$ the reactants are favoured. The further away from zero the value of $\Delta G^{\ominus}$, the further the equilibrium position lies to the right or left until, when $\Delta G^{\ominus} > 20$ to 30 kJ mol^{-1} or $\Delta G^{\ominus} < -20$ to -30 kJ mol^{-1}, the reaction can be regarded as virtually complete in one direction or the other. This is summed up in the following diagrams.

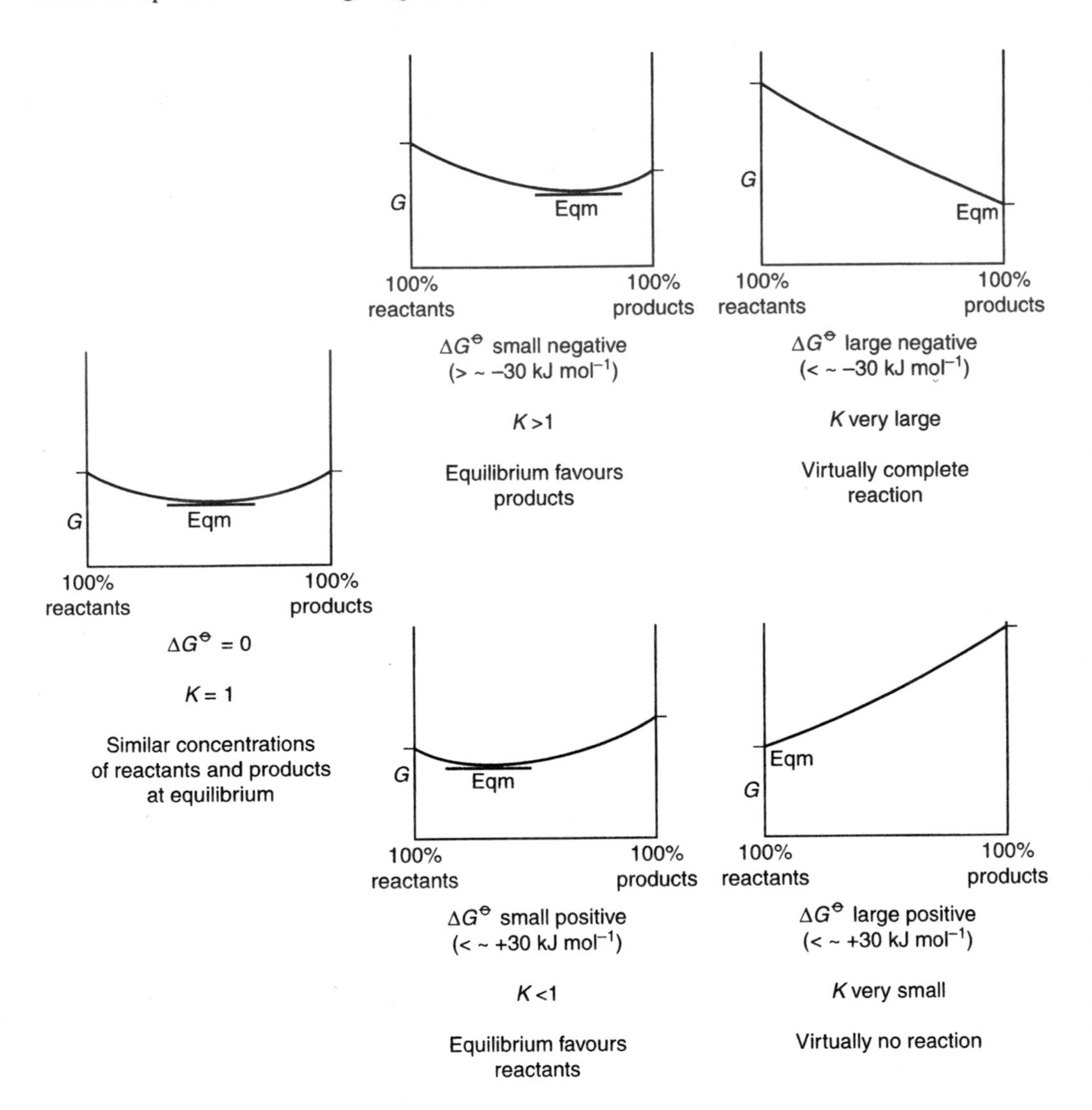

Notice that in every case G is at a minimum at equilibrium so that ΔG for a partial reaction to an equilibrium mixture is always negative, even when $\Delta G^{\ominus}$ (for complete reaction, under standard conditions) is positive.

In the next section we show you how the variation in equilibrium constant with temperature is related to the standard enthalpy change of reaction.

A2.3 The relationship between K and $\Delta H^{\ominus}$

To derive this relationship, you need only combine two equations which you already know.

$$\Delta G^{\ominus} = \Delta H^{\ominus} - T\Delta S^{\ominus}$$

and

$$\Delta G^{\circ} = -RT \ln K$$

Combining these two equations gives

$$-RT \ln K = \Delta H^{\circ} - T\Delta S^{\circ}$$

or

$$\ln K = -\frac{\Delta H^{\circ}}{RT} + \frac{\Delta S^{\circ}}{R}$$

ΔH° and ΔS° vary a little with temperature but can be treated as constants over a limited temperature range. A plot of ln K against $1/T$ should therefore be a straight line, because the equation is of the form

$$y = mx + c$$

where the slope

$$m = -\frac{\Delta H^{\circ}}{R}$$

and the intercept

$$c = \frac{\Delta S^{\circ}}{R}$$

We can therefore use a series of measurements of equilibrium constants at different temperatures in two important ways.

1. We can calculate a value for ΔH°. This method is often applied when calorimetry cannot be used.
2. We can obtain values of K for temperatures other than those at which measurements were taken.

We illustrate these two uses in the following exercises.

EXERCISE 82

Answers on page 103

Use the information in the table below for the reaction:

$$N_2O_4\,(g) \rightleftharpoons 2NO_2\,(g)$$

in answering the questions which follow.

T/K	$(1/T)/K^{-1}$	K_p/atm	log (K_p/atm)
350	2.86×10^{-3}	3.89	+0.59
400	2.50×10^{-3}	4.79×10^{1}	+1.68
450	2.22×10^{-3}	3.47×10^{2}	+2.54
500	2.00×10^{-3}	1.70×10^{3}	+3.23

a Plot a graph of log K_p (y-axis) against $1/T$ (x-axis).

b Measure the slope of the graph and so calculate ΔH° for this reaction. You may assume that ΔH° is constant over this temperature range.

c What is the value of log K_p for this reaction at:
i) 375 K,
ii) 475 K,
iii) 550 K?
What assumption must you make to determine log K_p at 550 K?
d Use the graph to determine the effect of an increase in temperature on the position of equilibrium for this reaction.

EXERCISE 83

Answers on page 104

Use the information in the table below for the reaction:

$$N_2\,(g) + 3H_2\,(g) \rightleftharpoons 2NH_3\,(g)$$

and answer the questions which follow.

T/K	$(1/T)$/K^{-1}	K_p/atm^{-2}	log (K_p/atm^{-2})
345	2.9×10^{-3}	1×10^{3}	+3.0
385	2.6×10^{-3}	3.16×10^{1}	+1.5
500	2.0×10^{-3}	3.55×10^{-2}	−1.45
700	1.43×10^{-3}	7.76×10^{-5}	−4.11

a Calculate $\Delta H^\ominus$ for the reaction by a graphical method.
b Use the graph to determine the effect of an increase in temperature on the position of equilibrium for this reaction.
c i) What do you notice about the gradients of the graphs drawn in this exercise and in the last?
ii) What determines whether the gradient will be positive or negative?

It is not always necessary to plot a graph of log K against $1/T$ in order to estimate K at some other temperature. We can derive an expression which enables you to calculate K directly.

Let K_1 = equilibrium constant at temperature T_1 and K_2 = equilibrium constant at temperature T_2. Then

$$\ln K_1 = -\frac{\Delta H^\ominus}{RT_1} + \frac{\Delta S^\ominus}{R}$$

and

$$\ln K_2 = -\frac{\Delta H^\ominus}{RT_2} + \frac{\Delta S^\ominus}{R}$$

Subtracting

$$\ln K_2 - \ln K_1 = -\frac{\Delta H^\ominus}{RT_2} + \frac{\Delta H^\ominus}{RT_1}$$

or

$$\ln\left(\frac{K_2}{K_1}\right) = \frac{\Delta H^\ominus}{R}\left(\frac{1}{T_1} - \frac{1}{T_2}\right)$$

If we use logarithms to the base 10, the expression becomes

$$\log\left(\frac{K_2}{K_1}\right) = \frac{\Delta H^\ominus}{2.30R}\left(\frac{1}{T_1} - \frac{1}{T_2}\right)$$

Thus, if four of the quantities $\Delta H^\ominus$, K_1, K_2, T_1, and T_2 are known, the fifth may be calculated.

Use the expression derived above in the following exercises.

EXERCISE 84

Answer on page 105

At 1065°C, $K_p = 0.0118$ atm for the reaction:

$$2H_2S\ (g) \rightleftharpoons 2H_2\ (g) + S_2\ (g);\ \Delta H^\ominus = 177.3\ \text{kJ mol}^{-1}$$

Calculate the equilibrium constant for the reaction at 1200°C.

EXERCISE 85

Answer on page 105

A particular reaction has a value of $K_p = 2.44$ atm at 1000 K and 3.74 atm at 1200 K. Calculate $\Delta H^\ominus$ for this reaction.

EXERCISE 86

Answers on page 106

The table below gives information about the values at different temperatures of the equilibrium constant for the reaction:

$$N_2\ (g) + O_2\ (g) \rightleftharpoons 2NO\ (g)$$

It also gives the partial pressures of NO in equilibrium with two different mixtures of nitrogen and oxygen at the given temperatures.

Temperature/K	$10^4 K_p$	Partial pressure of NO/atm × 10^2	
		$p_{N_2} = 0.8$ atm, $p_{O_2} = 0.2$ atm	$p_{N_2} = 0.8$ atm, $p_{O_2} = 0.05$ atm
1800	1.21	0.44	0.22
2000	4.08	0.81	0.40
2200	11.00	1.33	0.67
2400	25.10	2.00	1.00
2600	50.30	2.84	1.42

a Write an expression for the equilibrium constant, K_p, for the given reaction.
b Use the expression you have written to explain why the values in the fourth column are half those in the third.
c What condition of temperature and pressure should be used to obtain the best yield of NO? Justify your answer.
d Is the reaction exothermic or endothermic? Justify your answer.

EXERCISE 87

Answer on page 106

Calculate $\Delta H^\ominus$ from the data given in Exercise 86.

ANSWERS

(Answers to questions from examination papers are provided by ILPAC and not by the examination boards.)

EXERCISE 1

1. B
2. A
3. D
4. C
5. J
6. E, F, I or L
7. G, H or K
8. K
9. I
10. E, G or H
11. L

EXERCISE 2

Heterogeneous – A, B, C, D, G, H, J and K
Homogeneous – E, F, I and L

EXERCISE 3

Table 2

System	Equation	Constant macroscopic properties (examples)
A	$Br_2 (l) \rightleftharpoons Br_2 (g)$	Volume of liquid bromine Mass of bromine gas Colour of gas
B	$H_2O (l) \rightleftharpoons H_2O (s)$	Mass of solid ice Volume of water Volume of solid ice
C	$C_{12}H_{22}O_{11} (s) + aq \rightleftharpoons C_{12}H_{22}O_{11} (aq)$	Mass of solid sugar Concentration of solution Volume of solution
D	$I_2 (s) \rightleftharpoons I_2 (g)$	Mass of iodine crystals Colour of iodine vapour Mass of iodine vapour
E	$H_2 (g) + I_2 (g) \rightleftharpoons 2HI (g)$	Concentration of HI Mass of I_2 Amount of H_2
F	$CH_3CO_2H (l) + C_2H_5OH (l) \rightleftharpoons CH_3CO_2C_2H_5 (l) + H_2O (l)$	Mass of ethanol Amount of water Volume of liquid phase
G	$3Fe (s) + 4H_2O (g) \rightleftharpoons Fe_3O_4 (s) + 4H_2 (g)$	Mass of Fe_3O_4 Partial pressure of H_2 Partial pressure of H_2O
H	$Cu (s) \rightleftharpoons Cu^{2+} (aq) + 2e^-$	Mass of copper Amount of Cu^{2+} (aq) Colour of solution
I	$NH_3 (aq) + H_2O (l) \rightleftharpoons NH_4^+ (aq) + OH^- (aq)$ $NH_3 (g) + aq \rightleftharpoons NH_3 (aq)$	Concentration of OH^- (aq) Amount of NH_4^+ (aq) Partial pressure of NH_3
J	$I_2 (aq) \rightleftharpoons I_2 (CCl_3CH_3)$	Concentration of I_2 (aq) Mass of I_2 in CCl_3CH_3 Colour of solutions
K	$CaCO_3 (s) \rightleftharpoons Ca^{2+} (aq) + CO_3^{2-} (aq)$	Mass of solid $CaCO_3$ Concentration of Ca^{2+} (aq) Amount of CO_3^{2-} (aq)
L	$Cu^{2+} (aq) + 4NH_3 (aq) \rightleftharpoons [Cu(NH_3)_4]^{2+} (aq)$	Concentration of Cu^{2+} (aq) Colour of solution Amount of $Cu(NH_3)_4^{2+}$

EXERCISE 4

a A. Bromine vapour would escape continuously into the air by diffusion, and the liquid would evaporate to take its place. There can be no equilibrium if one or more of the components is continuously removed.

D. Iodine vapour would escape continuously into the air by diffusion and the solid would sublime to take its place. There can be no equilibrium if one or more of the components is removed.

E. All three gases would diffuse into the air at different rates. Their concentrations would never be constant and, therefore, the gases could never be in equilibrium.

G. Steam and hydrogen would escape continuously into the air by diffusion. There can be no equilibrium if one or more of the components is removed.

General answer: In all the systems shown in Fig. 5, at least one component would escape continuously into the air by diffusion if the system were not closed. The amount of at least one component present would decrease continuously until it is completely removed. Equilibrium cannot be maintained if the amounts of components are changing; still less if a component disappears! However, if the rate of escape is very slow, equilibrium may be effectively maintained long enough for practical purposes; e.g. during the course of an experiment.

b In system (K), the water would slowly evaporate and the amount of solid would increase so that, strictly speaking, equilibrium could not be maintained in an open tube. However, the change would hardly be detectable during the course of an observation so that for most practical purposes we can regard this system as being in equilibrium even when it is open.

EXERCISE 5

A. i) Put a little liquid bromine in a gas jar, cover with a gas jar plate and leave at room temperature.
ii) Fill a gas jar with warm bromine vapour, cover with a gas jar plate and cool.

B. i) Put water in a beaker and cool until some ice forms; then maintain the temperature at 0°C.
ii) Put a block of ice into a beaker and warm until some ice has melted; then maintain the temperature at 0°C.

C. i) Add sugar crystals to distilled water in a conical flask and stir to dissolve. When no more will dissolve, add a few extra crystals and seal the conical flask.
ii) Make a saturated sugar solution; leave in an open container or cool the solution until some sugar crystals precipitate. Then seal the flask.

D. i) Take a little solid iodine. Heat it on a combustion spoon. Transfer quickly to a gas jar and seal the jar with a gas jar plate.
ii) Heat some iodine in a container fitted with a bung and delivery tube. Pass the vapour into a gas jar, seal it and leave at room temperature.

F. i) Mix together some ethanoic acid and ethanol in a sealed container.
ii) Mix together some ethyl ethanoate and water in a sealed container.

G. i) Pass steam into an iron box.
ii) Pass hydrogen into an iron box containing some Fe_3O_4.

H. i) Place a copper strip in a beaker of dilute sulphuric acid. Set up an electrolysis cell with the copper strip as the anode and a piece of inert metal or carbon as the cathode. Pass a current through the cell until some of the copper metal has dissolved giving Cu^{2+} (aq) ions.
ii) Set up two metal or carbon electrodes in a solution of copper(II) sulphate solution, and pass a current until some of the copper has deposited on the cathode, effectively giving a copper strip.

I. i) Bubble ammonia gas into water.
ii) Mix an ammonium salt with an alkali in aqueous solution.

J. i) Into a measuring cylinder pour a solution of iodine in 1,1,1-trichloroethane followed by a similar volume of water.
ii) Into a measuring cylinder pour an aqueous solution of iodine followed by a similar volume of 1,1,1-trichloroethane.

K. i) *Shake solid calcium carbonate with sodium chloride solution.*
ii) Mix together solutions of calcium chloride and sodium carbonate.
L. i) Pour some copper(II) sulphate solution into a flask. Add concentrated ammonia solution, with shaking, until the pale blue precipitate which forms at first dissolves to give a deep blue solution.
ii) Dissolve solid tetraamminecopper(II) sulphate in water.

EXERCISE 6

One of several acceptable formulations of Le Chatelier's principle is as follows:

'If a system in equilibrium is subjected to a change which disturbs the equilibrium, the system responds in such a way as to counteract the effect of the change.'

EXPERIMENT 1

Specimen results

Results Table 1

Change	Observation	Cause	Inference
$[Fe^{3+}]$ increased	Darker colour	Concentration of $FeSCN^{2+}$ increases	Equilibrium shifts to the right
$[SCN^-]$ increased	Darker colour	Concentration of $FeSCN^{2+}$ increases	Equilibrium shifts to the right
$[Fe^{3+}]$ decreased	Lighter colour	Concentration of $FeSCN^{2+}$ decreases	Equilibrium shifts to the left

Questions

1. The position of equilbrium would shift to the left.
2. **a** The system counteracts the imposed change (an increase in $[Fe^{3+}]$) by converting some Fe^{3+} and some SCN^- to $FeSCN^{2+}$.
   b The system counteracts the imposed change (an increase in $[SCN^-]$) by converting some SCN^- and some Fe^{3+} to $FeSCN^{2+}$.
   c The system counteracts the imposed change (an decrease in $[Fe^{3+}]$) by converting $FeSCN^{2+}$ to Fe^{3+} and SCN^-.

EXERCISE 7

The position of equilibrium is defined by the concentrations of both liquid and gas present. Adding more liquid increases the **mass** of bromine but not its concentration. Therefore the equilibrium is not disturbed and the concentration of bromine gas remains the same.

Beware of applying Le Chatelier's principle without thinking about concentrations. It is false reasoning to say that the system responds to the imposed change by converting some of the added liquid to gas. The imposed change must directly affect the concentration of one or more components for there to be any response.

EXERCISE 8

Although the amount of solid copper changes, its concentration (or density in this case) does not change. Therefore there will be no change in the equilibrium position.

EXERCISE 9

Hot water. The mixture becomes darker in colour. This implies an increase in the concentration of NO_2, which is dark red/brown in colour (N_2O_4 has little colour). The imposed change is a transfer of energy from the surroundings, which increases the temperature of the system. The system responds by absorbing some of this energy in an endothermic reaction, i.e. the conversion of N_2O_4 to NO.
Cold water. The mixture becomes paler in colour, which implies a decrease in the concentration of NO_2. The imposed change is a loss of energy to the surroundings which decreases the temperature of the system. The system responds by releasing energy in an exothermic reaction, i.e. the conversion of NO_2 to N_2O_4.

EXERCISE 10

a Equilibrium shifts to the right – giving more products.
b Equilibrium shifts to the right – giving more products.
c Equilibrium shifts to the left – giving more reactants.
d Equilibrium shifts to the right – giving more products.
e No change, because a shift in neither direction can absorb energy to reduce the temperature.

EXERCISE 11

a i) Higher temperature favours the reactants in an exothermic reaction.
ii) Higher temperature favours the products in an endothermic reaction.
b i) Lower temperature favours the products in an exothermic reaction.
ii) Lower temperature favours the reactants in an endothermic reaction.

EXERCISE 12

a Equilibrium shifts to the right because this produces fewer gaseous molecules, so tending to reduce the pressure.
b Same as **a**.
c No change. As there are the same number of gaseous molecules on each side of the equation, a shift in neither direction can reduce the pressure.

EXERCISE 13

a No change. As there are the same number of **gaseous** molecules on each side of the equation, a shift in neither direction can increase the pressure.
b Same as **a**.
c Equilibrium shifts to the right because this produces more gaseous molecules, so tending to increase the pressure. Note that the pressure does not increase sufficiently to restore the original value. The important point here is that Le Chatelier's principle enables you to predict the **direction** of adjustment.

EXERCISE 14

a ... gaseous ...
b ... decrease ...
c ... increase ...
d ... the same ...

EXERCISE 15

a A catalyst is used to increase the **rate** at which equilibrium is achieved; it has no effect on the **position** of equilibrium. Low temperature and high pressure shift the equilibrium to the right.
b The same answer as in **a**.
c A catalyst is not used because a satisfactory rate is achieved without one. High temperature and low pressure shift the equilibrium to the right.

EXERCISE 16

a At low temperatures, equilibrium is not achieved rapidly enough for economical conversion.
b It is very expensive to run processes at high pressure. In this case the improvement in yield is not worth the extra cost. Also, high pressure tends to liquefy the sulphur dioxide.
c Running at low pressure is also expensive, and decreases the throughput of materials.

EXERCISE 17

a i) $K_c = \frac{[H_2\ (g)]\ [Br_2\ (g)]}{[HBr\ (g)]^2}$ no unit

ii) $K_c = \frac{[SO_3\ (g)]^2}{[SO_2\ (g)]^2\ [O_2\ (g)]}$ $dm^3\ mol^{-1}$

iii) $K_c = \frac{[Cu^{2+}\ (aq)]\ [NH_3\ (aq)]^4}{[Cu\ (NH_3)_4^{2+}\ (aq)]}$ $mol^4\ dm^{-12}$

iv) $K_c = \frac{[NO_2\ (g)]^2}{[NO\ (g)]^2\ [O_2\ (g)]}$ $dm^3\ mol^{-1}$

v) $K_c = \frac{[P_4\ (g)]\ [F_2\ (g)]^{10}}{[PF_5\ (g)]^4}$ $mol^7\ dm^{-21}$

vi) $K_c = \frac{[N_2\ (g)]\ [O_2\ (g)]}{[NO\ (g)]^2}$ no unit

vii) $K_c = \frac{[CH_3CO_2C_2H_5\ (l)]\ [H_2O\ (l)]}{[C_2H_5OH\ (l)]\ [CH_3CO_2H\ (l)]}$ no unit

b In equations i), vi) and vii) the same number of moles appears on each side of the equation. This means that the same number of concentration terms appears at the top and bottom of the equilibrium constant expressions, so that the units of concentration cancel.

EXERCISE 18

a $K_c = \frac{[CO\ (g)]\ [Cl_2\ (g)]}{[COCl_2\ (g)]}$ $K_c' = \frac{[COCl_2\ (g)]}{[CO\ (g)]\ [Cl_2\ (g)]}$

b $K_c = \frac{1}{K_c'}\ \left(\text{or } K_c' = \frac{1}{K_c}\right)$

EXERCISE 19

a $K_c = \frac{[NO_2\ (g)]}{[N_2O_4\ (g)]^{1/2}}$ $K_c' = \frac{[NO_2\ (g)]^2}{[N_2O_4\ (g)]}$

b Squaring K_c from **a** gives $K_c^2 = \frac{[NO_2\ (g)]^2}{[N_2O_4\ (g)]} = K_c'$

$\therefore$ at 100°C, $K_c = \sqrt{(K_c')} = (0.490\ mol\ dm^{-3})^{1/2} = \mathbf{0.700\ mol^{1/2}\ dm^{-3/2}}$
and at 200°C, $K_c = \sqrt{(K_c')} = (18.6\ mol\ dm^{-3})^{1/2} = \mathbf{4.31\ mol^{1/2}\ dm^{-3/2}}$

EXERCISE 20

$$K_c = \frac{[NO_2]^2}{[N_2O_4]} = \frac{(0.010\ mol\ dm^{-3})^2}{0.021\ mol\ dm^{-3}} = \mathbf{4.8 \times 10^{-3}\ mol\ dm^{-3}}$$

EXERCISE 21

a $[PCl_5\ (g)] = \frac{0.0042\ mol}{2.0\ dm^3} = 0.0021\ mol\ dm^{-3}$

$[Cl_2\ (g)] = [PCl_3\ (g)] = \frac{0.040\ mol}{2.0\ dm^3} = 0.020\ mol\ dm^{-3}$

$\therefore\ K_c = \frac{[PCl_3\ (g)][Cl_2\ (g)]}{[PCl_5\ (g)]} = \frac{(0.020\ mol\ dm^{-3})^2}{0.0021\ mol\ dm^{-3}} = \mathbf{0.19\ mol\ dm^{-3}}$

b i) When K_c is large, the concentrations of products are greater than the concentrations of reactants.
ii) When K_c is small, the concentrations of products are smaller than the concentrations of reactants.

EXERCISE 22

a $H_2 (g) + I_2 (g) \rightleftharpoons 2HI (g)$

b $$K_c = \frac{[HI (g)]^2}{[H_2 (g)] [I_2 (g)]}$$

c Mixture 1. $$K_c = \frac{(0.1715 \text{ mol}/1.00 \text{ dm}^3)^2}{(0.02265 \text{ mol}/1.00 \text{ dm}^3) \times (0.02840 \text{ mol}/1.00 \text{ dm}^3)}$$

$$= \frac{0.02941 \text{ mol}^2 \text{ dm}^{-6}}{6.433 \times 10^{-4} \text{ mol}^2 \text{ dm}^{-6}} = \mathbf{45.72}$$

Mixture 2. $$K_c = \frac{(0.1779 \text{ mol}/1.00 \text{ dm}^3)^2}{(0.01699 \text{ mol}/1.00 \text{ dm}^3) \times (0.04057 \text{ mol}/1.00 \text{ dm}^3)}$$

$$= \frac{0.03165 \text{ mol}^2 \text{ dm}^{-6}}{6.893 \times 10^{-4} \text{ mol}^2 \text{ dm}^{-6}} = \mathbf{45.92}$$

d $$K_c = \frac{(0.1715 \text{ mol}/2.00 \text{ dm}^3)^2}{(0.02265 \text{ mol}/2.00 \text{ dm}^3) \times (0.02840 \text{ mol}/2.00 \text{ dm}^3)}$$

$$= \frac{7.353 \times 10^{-3} \text{ mol}^2 \text{ dm}^{-6}}{1.608 \times 10^{-4} \text{ mol}^2 \text{ dm}^{-6}} = \mathbf{45.72}$$

(Did you notice the short cut? 2.00 dm^3 cancels, giving the same expression as in part **a**.)

e $$K_c = \frac{(0.1779 \text{ mol}/V \text{ dm}^3)^2}{(0.01699 \text{ mol}/V \text{ dm}^3) \times (0.04057 \text{ mol}/V \text{ dm}^3)}$$

$$= \frac{(0.1779 \text{ mol})^2}{0.01699 \times 0.04057 \text{ mol}} \times \frac{V^2 \text{ dm}^6}{V^2 \text{ dm}^6} = \mathbf{45.92}$$

EXPERIMENT 2

Specimen results

Results Table 2

Tube number	**1a**	**1b**	**2**	**3**	**4**
Mass of empty tube/g	12.01	12.24	12.57	12.18	12.73
Volume of HCl (aq) added/cm^3	5.0	5.0	5.0	5.0	5.0
Mass of tube after addition/g	17.03	17.34	17.77	17.35	17.92
Volume of ethyl ethanoate added/cm^3	–	–	5.0	4.0	2.0
Mass of tube after addition/g			22.28	20.99	19.78
Volume of water added/cm^3	–	–	–	1.0	3.0
Mass of tube after addition/g				21.98	22.78
Mass of ethyl ethanoate added/g			4.51	3.64	1.86
Mass of HCl (aq) added/g			5.20	5.17	5.19
Mass of water added/g				0.99	3.00

Results Table 3

Solution in flask	Equilibrium mixture				
Solution in burette	Sodium hydroxide 0.974 mol dm^{-3}				
Indicator	Phenolphthalein				
Tube number	1a	1b	2	3	4
Final burette reading	9.95	20.05	41.30	39.20	27.25
Initial burette reading	0.00	9.95	0.00	0.00	0.00
Titre/cm^3	9.95	10.10	41.30	39.20	27.25

Results Table 4

Tube number	2	3	4
1. Amount of HCl/mol	0.0100	0.0100	0.0100
2. Total amount of acid at eqm/mol	0.0413	0.0392	0.0273
3. Eqm amount of ethanoic acid/mol	0.0313	0.0292	0.0173
4. Eqm amount of ethanol/mol	0.0313	0.0292	0.0173
5. Initial amount of ethyl ethanoate/mol	0.0511	0.0413	0.0211
6. Eqm amount of ethyl ethanoate/mol	0.0198	0.0121	0.0038
7. Mass of pure HCl/g	0.365	0.365	0.365
8. Mass of water in HCl (aq)/g	4.84	4.81	4.83
9. Initial amount of water/mol	0.269	0.322	0.435
10. Eqm amount of water/mol	0.238	0.293	0.418
11. Eqm constant, K_c	0.204	0.240	0.19

Questions

1. According to Le Chatelier's principle, increasing the concentration of a reactant and decreasing the concentration of a product should both result in the shifting of the equilibrium position to the right. Therefore both the addition of water and titration with alkali should result in more ethanoic acid and ethanol being formed.
2. Dilution of the equilibrium mixture with water slows down both the forward and backward reactions (sometimes this is referred to as 'freezing the equilibrium'). Therefore the equilibrium position changes so slowly that there is time to complete the titration before the equilibrium is disturbed.

EXERCISE 23

$$N_2O_4 \rightleftharpoons 2NO_2$$

Equilibrium concn/mol dm^{-3} $\quad x \quad 1.85 \times 10^{-3}$

$$K_c = \frac{[NO_2]^2}{[N_2O_4]}$$

$$\therefore\ 1.06 \times 10^{-5}\ \text{mol dm}^{-3} = \frac{(1.85 \times 10^{-3}\ \text{mol dm}^{-3})^2}{x\ \text{mol dm}^{-3}}$$

$$\therefore\ x = \frac{(1.85 \times 10^{-3})^2}{(1.06 \times 10^{-5})} = 0.323$$

and $[N_2O_4]$ = **0.323 mol dm^{-3}**

EXERCISE 24

$$2H_2S\,(g) \rightleftharpoons 2H_2\,(g) + S_2\,(g)$$

Equilibrium concn/mol dm^{-3}	4.84×10^{-3}	x	2.33×10^{-3}

$$K_c = \frac{[H_2\,(g)]^2\,[S_2\,(g)]}{[H_2S\,(g)]^2}$$

$$2.25\times10^{-4}\ \text{mol dm}^{-3} = \frac{(x\ \text{mol dm}^{-3})^2 \times (2.33\times10^{-3}\ \text{mol dm}^{-3})}{(4.84\times10^{-3}\ \text{mol dm}^{-3})^2}$$

$$x^2 = \frac{(2.25\times10^{-4})(4.84\times10^{-3})^2}{(2.33\times10^{-3})} = 2.26\times10^{-6}$$

$$x = \sqrt{2.26\times10^{-6}} = 1.50\times10^{-3}$$

$$\therefore [H_2\,(g)] = \mathbf{1.50\times10^{-3}\ mol\ dm^{-3}}$$

EXERCISE 25

$$PCl_5\,(g) \rightleftharpoons PCl_3\,(g) + Cl_2\,(g)$$

a

Equilibrium amount/mol	x	0.15	0.090

$$K_c = \frac{[PCl_3\,(g)][Cl_2\,(g)]}{[PCl_5\,(g)]}$$

Substituting concentrations gives

$$0.19\ \text{mol dm}^{-3} = \frac{(0.15\ \text{mol}/2.0\ \text{dm}^3)(0.090\ \text{mol}/2.0\ \text{dm}^3)}{(x\ \text{mol}/2.0\ \text{dm}^3)}$$

$$\text{i.e. } 0.19 = \frac{0.075\times0.045}{x/2.0} = \frac{0.075\times0.045\times2.0}{x}$$

$$\therefore\ x = \frac{0.075\times0.045\times2.0}{0.19} = 0.0355$$

$$\therefore\ \text{amount of } PCl_5 = \mathbf{0.036\ mol}$$

b mass = amount × molar mass
= 0.0355 mol × 208.5 g mol^{-1} = **7.40 g**

EXERCISE 26

Amount of pentene at equilibrium = initial amount – amount reacted
= $(0.020 - 9.0 \times 10^{-3})$ mol = 0.011 mol

Amount of ethanoic acid at equilibrium = initial amount – amount reacted
= $(0.010 - 9.0 \times 10^{-3})$ mol = 1.0×10^{-3} mol

	CH_3CO_2H	+ C_5H_{10}	$\rightleftharpoons$ $CH_3CO_2C_5H_{11}$
Initial amount/mol	0.010	0.020	0
Equilibrium amount/mol	1.0×10^{-3}	0.011	9.0×10^{-3}

$$K_c = \frac{[CH_3CO_2C_5H_{11}]}{[CH_3CO_2H][C_5H_{10}]}$$

$$= \frac{(9.0\times10^{-3}\ \text{mol}/0.600\ \text{dm}^3)}{(1.0\times10^{-3}\ \text{mol}/0.600\ \text{dm}^3)\times(0.011\ \text{mol}/0.600\ \text{dm}^3)} = \mathbf{491\ dm^3\ mol^{-1}}$$

EXERCISE 27

Initial amount/mol	1.90	1.90	0
	H_2 (g) +	I_2 (g) ⇌	2HI (g)
Equilibrium amount/mol	(0.40)	(0.40)	(Calculation below)

Amount of H_2 at equilibrium = initial amount – amount reacted.

The equation shows that 2 mol of HI requires 1 mol of H_2 to react.
∴ to produce 3.00 mol of HI, the amount of H_2 reacted = 1.50 mol

Amount of H_2 at equilibrium = 1:90 mol – 1.50 mol = 0.40 mol

The calculation for I_2 is the same. Since the equation has equal numbers of moles on each side, we can substitute amounts rather than concentrations in the equilibrium law expression. (Volume cancels.)

$$K_c = \frac{[\text{HI (g)}]^2}{[\text{H}_2\text{ (g)}][\text{I}_2\text{ (g)}]} = \frac{(3.00\text{ mol})^2}{(0.40\text{ mol})\times(0.40\text{ mol})} = \mathbf{56}$$

EXERCISE 28

$$\text{Initial amount of CH}_3\text{CO}_2\text{H} = \frac{6.0\text{ g}}{60.1\text{ g mol}^{-1}} = 0.10\text{ mol}$$

$$\text{Initial amount of C}_2\text{H}_5\text{OH} = \frac{6.9\text{ g}}{46.1\text{ g mol}^{-1}} = 0.15\text{ mol}$$

$$\text{Equilibrium amount of CH}_3\text{CO}_2\text{C}_2\text{H}_5 = \frac{7.0\text{ g}}{88.1\text{ g mol}^{-1}} = 0.079\text{ mol}$$

The equation shows that the equilibrium amount of H_2O is also 0.079 mol, and that this is formed from an equal amount of CH_3CO_2H or C_2H_5OH.

Equilibrium amount of CH_3CO_2H = initial amount – amount reacted.
= 0.10 mol – 0.079 mol = 0.021 mol

Equilibrium amount of C_2H_5OH = 0.15 mol – 0.079 mol = 0.071 mol

Initial Initial amount/mol	0.10	0.15	0	0
	CH_3CO_2H +	C_2H_5OH ⇌	$CH_3CO_2C_2H_5$ +	H_2O
Equilibrium amount/mol	0.021	0.071	0.079	0.079

Since the equation has equal numbers of moles on each side, we can substitute amounts rather than concentrations in the equilibrium law expression.

$$K_c = \frac{[\text{CH}_3\text{CO}_2\text{C}_2\text{H}_5][\text{H}_2\text{O}]}{[\text{CH}_3\text{CO}_2\text{H}][\text{C}_2\text{H}_5\text{OH}]} = \frac{(0.079)^2}{0.021\times 0.071} = \mathbf{4.2}$$

EXERCISE 29

Initial amount/mol	3.0	3.0	0	0
	$CO\ (g) + H_2O\ (g) \rightleftharpoons CO_2\ (g) + H_2\ (g)$			
Equilibrium amount/mol	$3.0 - x$	$3.0 - x$	x	x

$$K_c = \frac{[CO_2\ (g)][H_2\ (g)]}{[CO\ (g)][H_2O\ (g)]}$$

$$4.00 = \frac{(x \text{ mol})\ (x \text{ mol})}{(3.0 - x) \text{ mol}\ (3.0 - x) \text{ mol}} = \frac{x^2}{(3.0 - x)^2}$$

Taking the square root of both sides,

$$2.00 = \frac{x}{3.0 - x}$$

$$\therefore\ 6.0 - 2.0x = x \text{ or } 3x = 6.0$$

$\therefore\ x = 2.0$ and amount of hydrogen $=$ **2.0 mol**

EXERCISE 30

$$\text{Amount of } PCl_5 = \frac{2.085 \text{ g}}{208.5 \text{ g mol}^{-1}} = 0.0100 \text{ mol}$$

Initial amount/mol	0.0100	0	0
	$PCl_5\ (g) \rightleftharpoons PCl_3\ (g) + Cl_2\ (g)$		
Equilibrium amount/mol	$0.0100 - x$	x	x

$$K_c = \frac{[PCl_3\ (g)][Cl_2\ (g)]}{[PCl_5\ (g)]}$$

$$0.19 \text{ mol dm}^{-3} = \frac{\left(\frac{x}{0.500} \text{ mol dm}^{-3}\right)\left(\frac{x}{0.500} \text{ mol dm}^{-3}\right)}{\left(\frac{0.0100 - x}{0.500} \text{ mol dm}^{-3}\right)}$$

$$0.19 = \frac{x^2}{0.500(0.0100 - x)} = \frac{x^2}{0.00500 - 0.500x}$$

$$9.5 \times 10^{-4} - 0.095x = x^2 \text{ or } x^2 + 0.095x - (9.5 \times 10^{-4}) = 0$$

$$x = \frac{-b \pm \sqrt{b^2 - 4ac}}{2a} \text{ where } a = 1,\ b = 0.095 \text{ and } c = -(9.5 \times 10^{-4})$$

$$x = \frac{-0.095 \pm \sqrt{(0.095)^2 + (4 \times 9.5 \times 10^{-4})}}{2}$$

$$2x = -0.095 \pm \sqrt{(9.025 \times 10^{-3}) + (3.8 \times 10^{-3})}$$

$$= -0.095 \pm \sqrt{1.2825 \times 10^{-2}} = -0.095 \pm 0.1132$$

$$\therefore x = 0.0091 \text{ or } -0.1041 \text{ (absurd root)}$$

$$[PCl_5\ (g)] = \frac{(0.0100 - 0.0091) \text{ mol}}{0.500 \text{ dm}^3} = \mathbf{1.8 \times 10^{-3}\ mol\ dm^{-3}}$$

$$[Cl_2\ (g)] = [PCl_3\ (g)] = \frac{0.0091 \text{ mol}}{0.500 \text{ dm}^3} = \mathbf{1.8 \times 10^{-2}\ mol\ dm^{-3}}$$

EXERCISE 31

Initial amount/mol	2.00	2.00	0
	H_2 (g) +	I_2 (g) ⇌	2HI (g)
Equilibrium amount/mol	$2.00 - x$	$2.00 - x$	$2x$

$$K_c = \frac{[\text{HI (g)}]^2}{[\text{H}_2\text{ (g)}]\,[\text{I}_2\text{ (g)}]}$$

$$49.0 = \frac{(2x)^2}{(2.00 - x)\,(2.00 - x)}$$

Taking the square roots, $\pm 7.00 = \dfrac{2x}{2.00 - x}$

$$14.0 - 7.00x = 2x$$

$$9.00x = 14.0 \text{ and } x = 1.56$$

∴ amount of HI = $2x$ mol = **3.12 mol**

Amount of H_2 = amount of I_2 = $(2.00 - x)$ = **0.44 mol**

EXERCISE 32

$$\text{Initial amount of ethanol} = \frac{50.0\text{ g}}{46.1\text{ g mol}^{-1}} = 1.08\text{ mol}$$

$$\text{Initial amount of propanoic acid} = \frac{50.0\text{ g}}{74.1\text{ g mol}^{-1}} = 0.675\text{ mol}$$

Initial amount/mol	1.08	0.675	0	0
	C_2H_5OH (l) +	$C_2H_5CO_2H$ (l) ⇌	$C_2H_5CO_2C_2H_5$ (l) +	H_2O (l)
Equilibrium amount/mol	$1.08 - x$	$0.675 - x$	x	x

$$K_c = \frac{[\text{C}_2\text{H}_5\text{CO}_2\text{C}_2\text{H}_5\text{ (l)}][\text{H}_2\text{O (l)}]}{[\text{C}_2\text{H}_5\text{OH (l)}][\text{C}_2\text{H}_5\text{CO}_2\text{H (l)}]}$$

$$7.5 = \frac{x \times x}{(1.08 - x)\,(0.675 - x)} = \frac{x^2}{0.729 - 1.755x + x^2}$$

$$5.47 - 13.16x + 7.5x^2 = x^2$$

$$6.5x^2 - 13.16x + 5.47 = 0$$

$$x = \frac{-b \pm \sqrt{b^2 - 4ac}}{2a}$$

$$= \frac{13.16 \pm \sqrt{(13.16)^2 - (4 \times 6.5 \times 5.47)}}{2 \times 6.5}$$

$$x = \frac{13.16 \pm \sqrt{173.2 - 142.2}}{2 \times 6.5}$$

$$= \frac{13.16 \pm \sqrt{31.0}}{13} = \frac{13.16 \pm 5.57}{13}$$

∴ $x = 0.584$ or 1.44 (absurd root)

∴ amount of ethyl propanoate = 0.584 mol

and mass of ethyl propanoate = 0.584 mol × 102.1 g mol^{-1} = **59.6 g**

EXERCISE 33

a $K_p = \frac{p_{N_2} \times p_{H_2}^3}{p_{NH_3}^2}$ atm^2

b $K_p = \frac{p_{SO_3}^2}{p_{SO_2}^2 \times p_{O_2}}$ atm^{-1}

c $K_p = \frac{p_{CO}^2}{p_{CO_2}}$ atm

d $K_p = p_{CO_2}$ atm

e $K_p = p_{NH_3} \times p_{H_2S}$ atm^2

Note that the partial pressure of a solid is taken to be constant (like its concentration) and does not therefore appear in the equilibrium expression.

EXERCISE 34

$$K_p = \frac{p_{SO_3}^2}{p_{SO_2}^2 \times p_{O_2}} = \frac{(4.5\text{ atm})^2}{(0.090\text{ atm})^2 \times 0.083\text{ atm}} = \mathbf{3.01 \times 10^4\ atm^{-1}}$$

EXERCISE 35

a

$$\text{Amount of } H_2 = \frac{12.8\text{ g}}{2.02\text{ g mol}^{-1}} = 6.34\text{ mol}$$

$$\text{Amount of } NH_3 = \frac{25.1\text{ g}}{17.0\text{ g mol}^{-1}} = 1.48\text{ mol}$$

$$\text{Amount of } N_2 = \frac{59.6\text{ g}}{28.0\text{ g mol}^{-1}} = 2.13\text{ mol}$$

$$\text{Total amount} = (6.34 + 1.48 + 2.13)\text{ mol} = 9.95\text{ mol}$$

$$X_{H_2} = \frac{\text{amount of } H_2}{\text{total amount}} = \frac{6.34\text{ mol}}{9.95\text{ mol}} = \mathbf{0.640}$$

$$X_{NH_3} = \frac{1.48\text{ mol}}{9.95\text{ mol}} = \mathbf{0.149}$$

$$X_{N_2} = \frac{2.13\text{ mol}}{9.95\text{ mol}} = \mathbf{0.214}$$

b

Partial pressure = mole fraction × total pressure

$$p_{H_2} = 0.640 \times 10.0\text{ atm} = \mathbf{6.40\ atm}$$

$$p_{NH_3} = 0.149 \times 10.0\text{ atm} = \mathbf{1.49\ atm}$$

$$p_{N_2} = 0.214 \times 10.0\text{ atm} = \mathbf{2.14\ atm}$$

c

$$K_p = \frac{p_{NH_3}^2}{p_{N_2} \times p_{H_2}^3} = \frac{(1.49\text{ atm})^2}{2.14\text{ atm} \times (6.40\text{ atm})^3} = \mathbf{3.96 \times 10^{-3}\ atm^{-2}}$$

EXERCISE 36

Total amount of gas = (0.33 + 0.67 + 0.67) mol = 1.67 mol
Partial pressure = mole fraction × total pressure

$$p_{PCl_5} = \frac{0.33\text{ mol}}{1.67\text{ mol}} \times 10.0\text{ atm} = 1.98\text{ atm}$$

$$p_{PCl_3} = p_{Cl_2} = \frac{0.67\text{ mol}}{1.67\text{ mol}} \times 10.0\text{ atm} = 4.01\text{ atm}$$

$$K_p = \frac{p_{PCl_3} \times p_{Cl_2}}{p_{PCl_5}} = \frac{4.01\text{ atm} \times 4.01\text{ atm}}{1.98\text{ atm}} = \mathbf{8.12\ atm}$$

EXERCISE 37

Total amount of gas = (0.224 + 0.142) mol = 0.366 mol
Partial pressure = mole fraction × total pressure

$$p_{CO_2} = \frac{0.224}{0.366} \times 1.83 \text{ atm} = \mathbf{1.12 \text{ atm}}$$

$$p_{NH_3} = \frac{0.142}{0.366} \times 1.83 \text{ atm} = \mathbf{0.710 \text{ atm}}$$

$$K_p = p_{NH_3}^2 \times p_{CO_2} = (0.710 \text{ atm})^2 \times 1.12 \text{ atm} = \mathbf{0.565 \text{ atm}^3}$$

EXERCISE 38

$$\text{Amount of } SO_3 \text{ at equilibrium} = 2.00 \text{ mol} \times \frac{20}{100} = 0.40 \text{ mol}$$

	$2SO_2$ (g)	+ O_2 (g)	⇌ $2SO_3$ (g)
Initial amount/mol	2.0	2.0	0
Equilibrium amount/mol	1.60	1.80	0.40

Total amount of gas = (1.60 + 1.80 + 0.40) mol = 3.80 mol

$$p_{SO_3} = X_{SO_3} p_T = \frac{0.40}{3.80} \times p_T$$

$$p_{SO_2} = \frac{1.60}{3.80} \times p_T \qquad p_{O_2} = \frac{1.80}{3.80} \times p_T$$

$$K_p = \frac{p_{SO_3}^2}{p_{SO_2}^2 \times p_{O_2}}$$

$$0.13 \text{ atm}^{-1} = \frac{(0.40/3.80)^2 p_T^2}{(1.60/3.80)^2 p_T^2 (1.80/3.80) p_T} = \frac{0.0111}{0.177 \times 0.474 p_T}$$

$$p_T = \frac{0.0111}{0.13 \text{ atm}^{-1} \times 0.177 \times 0.474} = \mathbf{1.02 \text{ atm}}$$

EXERCISE 39

	$2SO_2$ (g)	+ O_2 (g)	⇌ $2SO_3$ (g)
Initial amount/mol	2	1	0
Equilibrium amount/mol	4/3	2/3	2/3

Total amount of gas = 4/3 + 2/3 + 2/3 = 8/3
Partial pressure = mole fraction × total pressure

$$p_{SO_3} = \frac{(2/3)}{(8/3)} \times 9 \text{ atm} = 9/4 \text{ atm}$$

$$p_{SO_2} = \frac{(4/3)}{(8/3)} \times 9 \text{ atm} = 9/2 \text{ atm}$$

$$p_{O_2} = \frac{(2/3)}{(8/3)} \times 9 \text{ atm} = 9/4 \text{ atm}$$

$$K_p = \frac{p_{SO_3}^2}{p_{SO_2}^2 \times p_{O_2}} = \frac{(9/4)^2 \text{ atm}^2}{(9/2)^2 \text{ atm}^2 \times 9/4 \text{ atm}} = \frac{1}{9} \text{ atm}^{-1} = \mathbf{0.11 \text{ atm}^{-1}}$$

EXERCISE 40

Amount of N_2O_4 at equilibrium = initial mount – amount reacted
= (1.00 – 0.66) mol = 0.34 mol

Amount of NO_2 formed = 2 × amount N_2O_4 reacted
= 2 × 0.66 mol = 1.32 mol

Initial amount/mol	1.00	0
	N_2O_4 (g) ⇌	$2NO_2$ (g)
Equilibrium amount/mol	0.34	1.32

Total amount of gas = (0.34 + 1.32) mol = 1.66 mol

Partial pressure = mole fraction × total pressure

$$p_{N_2O_4} = \frac{0.34\text{ mol}}{1.66\text{ mol}} \times 98.3\text{ kPa} = 20.1\text{ kPa}$$

$$p_{NO_2} = \frac{1.32\text{ mol}}{1.66\text{ mol}} \times 98.3\text{ kPa} = 78.2\text{ kPa}$$

$$K_p = \frac{p^2_{NO_2}}{p_{N_2O_4}} = \frac{(78.2\text{ kPa})^2}{20.1\text{ kPa}} = \mathbf{304\text{ kPa}}$$

Since 100 kPa = 760 mmHg = 1.00 atm

$$K_p = 304\text{ kPa} \times \frac{760\text{ mmHg}}{100\text{ kPa}} = \mathbf{2310\text{ mmHg}}$$

and

$$K_p = 304\text{ kPa} \times \frac{1.00\text{ atm}}{100\text{ kPa}} = \mathbf{3.04\text{ atm}}$$

EXERCISE 41

a

	$2NO_2$ (g) ⇌	$2NO$ (g) +	O_2 (g)
Equilibrium amount/mol	0.96	0.040	0.020

Total amount of gas = (0.96 + 0.04 + 0.02) mol = 1.02 mol

$$p_{NO_2} = \frac{0.96}{1.02} \times 0.20\text{ atm} = 0.19\text{ atm}$$

$$p_{NO} = \frac{0.040}{1.02} \times 0.20\text{ atm} = 0.0078\text{ atm}$$

$$p_{O_2} = \frac{0.02}{1.02} \times 0.20\text{ atm} = 0.0039\text{ atm}$$

$$K_p = \frac{p^2_{NO} \times p_{O_2}}{p^2_{NO_2}} = \frac{0.0078^2\text{ atm}^2 \times 0.0039\text{ atm}}{0.19^2\text{ atm}^2} = \mathbf{6.6 \times 10^{-6}\text{ atm}}$$

b Average molar mass = $X_{NO_2} M_{NO_2} + X_{NO} M_{NO} + X_{O_2} M_{O_2}$

$$\left(\frac{0.96}{1.02} \times 46.0\text{ g mol}^{-1}\right) + \left(\frac{0.040}{1.02} \times 30.0\text{ g mol}^{-1}\right) + \left(\frac{0.020}{1.02} \times 32.0\text{ g mol}^{-1}\right)$$

$$= (43.3 + 1.18 + 0.63)\text{ g mol}^{-1} = \mathbf{45.1\text{ g mol}^{-1}}$$

EXERCISE 42

a $M_{avg} = X_{CO}M_{CO} + X_{CO_2}M_{CO_2}$
Since $X_{CO} + X_{CO_2} = 1$, $X_{CO_2} = 1 - X_{CO}$
$36\text{ g mol}^{-1} = (X_{CO} \times 28\text{ g mol}^{-1}) + (1 - X_{CO}) \times 44\text{ g mol}^{-1}$
$36 = 28X_{CO} + 44 - 44X_{CO}$

$$X_{CO} = \frac{44-36}{44-28} = \frac{8}{16} = \mathbf{0.5}$$

b $p_{CO} = X_{CO}p_T = 0.5 \times 12\text{ atm} = 6\text{ atm}$
$p_{CO_2} = X_{CO_2}p_T = 0.5 \times 12\text{ atm} = 6\text{ atm}$

$$K_p = \frac{p_{CO}^2}{p_{CO_2}} = \frac{(6\text{ atm})^2}{6\text{ atm}} = \mathbf{6\ atm}$$

c Let $x = X_{CO}$ and $1 - x = X_{CO_2}$

$$K_p = \frac{(X_{CO} \times p_T)^2}{X_{CO_2} \times p_T}$$

$$\therefore\ 6\text{ atm} = \frac{(x \times 2\text{ atm})^2}{(1-x) \times 2\text{ atm}} \text{ or } 6 = \frac{2x^2}{1-x}$$

$$\therefore\ 2x^2 = 6 - 6x$$

$$x^2 + 3x - 3 = 0$$

$$x = \frac{-3 \pm \sqrt{9+12}}{2} = 0.8 \text{ or } -3.8 \text{ (absurd root)}$$

$$\therefore\ X_{CO} = \mathbf{0.8}$$

EXERCISE 43

a i) $K_p = \frac{p_{HI}^2}{p_{H_2} \times p_{I_2}}$ ii) $K_p = \frac{p_{NO}^2}{p_{N_2} \times p_{O_2}}$

iii) $K_p = \frac{p_{NH_3}^2}{p_{N_2} \times p_{H_2}^3}$

b In each case the equilibrium shift is in the direction corresponding to an endothermic change, because that absorbs some of the energy introduced to raise the temperature.
i) To the left.
ii) To the right.
iii) To the left.

c i) K_p decreases (more reactants)
ii) K_p increases (more products)
iii) K_p decreases (more reactants)

d The equilibrium system with the largest numerical value of $\Delta H^{\ominus}$ might be expected to show the greatest variation in K_p with temperature change, i.e. system ii).

EXERCISE 44

a $K_s = [Ba^{2+}\text{ (aq)}][SO_4^{2-}\text{ (aq)}]\text{ mol}^2\text{ dm}^{-6}$
b $K_s = [Ca^{2+}\text{ (aq)}][F^-\text{ (aq)}]^2\text{ mol}^3\text{ dm}^{-9}$
c $K_s = [Ag^+\text{ (aq)}]^3[PO_4^{3-}\text{ (aq)}]\text{ mol}^4\text{ dm}^{-12}$

EXERCISE 45

a

$$CdCO_3\ (s) \rightleftharpoons Cd^{2+}\ (aq) + CO_3^{2-}\ (aq)$$

Equilibrium concn/mol dm^{-3} $\qquad 1.58 \times 10^{-7} \quad 1.58 \times 10^{-7}$

$$K_s = [Cd^{2+}\ (aq)]\ [CO_3{}^{2-}\ (aq)] = 1.58 \times 10^{-7}\ \text{mol dm}^{-3} \times 1.58 \times 10^{-7}\ \text{mol dm}^{-3}$$
$$= \mathbf{2.50 \times 10^{-14}\ mol^2\ dm^{-6}}$$

b

$$CaF_2\ (s) \rightleftharpoons Ca^{2+}\ (aq) + 2F^-\ (aq)$$

Equilibrium concn/mol dm^{-3} $\qquad 2.15 \times 10^{-4} \quad 2 \times 2.15 \times 10^{-4}$

$$K_s = [Ca^{2+}\ (aq)]\ [F^-\ (aq)]^2 = 2.15 \times 10^{-4}\ \text{mol dm}^{-3} \times (4.30 \times 10^{-4}\ \text{mol dm}^{-3})^2$$
$$= \mathbf{3.98 \times 10^{-11}\ mol^3\ dm^{-9}}$$

c

$$Cr(OH)_3\ (s) \rightleftharpoons Cr^{3+}\ (aq) + 3OH^-\ (aq)$$

Equilibrium concn/mol dm^{-3} $\qquad 1.39 \times 10^{-8} \quad 3 \times 1.39 \times 10^{-8}$

$$K_s = [Cr^{3+}\ (aq)]\ [OH^-\ (aq)]^3 = 1.39 \times 10^{-8}\ \text{mol dm}^{-3} \times (3 \times 1.39 \times 10^{-8}\ \text{mol dm}^{-3})^3$$
$$= \mathbf{1.01 \times 10^{-30}\ mol^4\ dm^{-12}}$$

EXERCISE 46

a

$$CuS\ (s) \rightleftharpoons Cu^{2+}\ (aq) + S^{2-}\ (aq)$$

Equilibrium concn/mol dm^{-3} $\qquad x \qquad x$

$$K_s = [Cu^{2+}\ (aq)]\ [S^{2-}\ (aq)]$$
$$6.3 \times 10^{-36}\ \text{mol}^2\ \text{dm}^{-6} = x\ \text{mol dm}^{-3} \times x\ \text{mol dm}^{-3}$$
$$x^2 = 6.3 \times 10^{-36} \qquad \therefore\ x = 2.5 \times 10^{-18}$$

and solubility = $\mathbf{2.5 \times 10^{-18}}$ **mol dm^{-3}**

b

$$Fe(OH)_2\ (s) \rightleftharpoons Fe^{2+}\ (aq) + 2OH^-\ (aq)$$

Equilibrium concn/mol dm^{-3} $\qquad x \qquad 2x$

$$K_s = [Fe^{2+}\ (aq)]\ [OH^-\ (aq)]^2$$

$6.0 \times 10^{-15}\ \text{mol}^3\ \text{dm}^{-9} = x\ \text{mol dm}^{-3} \times (2x\ \text{mol dm}^{-3})^2$
$\therefore\ 4x^3 = 6.0 \times 10^{-15}$
$x = (1.5 \times 10^{-15})^{1/3} = 1.1 \times 10^{-5}$
and solubility = $\mathbf{1.1 \times 10^{-5}}$ **mol dm^{-3}**

c

$$Ag_3PO_4\ (s) \rightleftharpoons 3Ag^+\ (aq) + PO_4^{3-}\ (aq)$$

Equilibrium concn/mol dm^{-3} $\qquad 3x \qquad x$

$$K_s = [Ag^+\ (aq)]^3\ [PO_4^{3-}\ (aq)]$$

$1.25 \times 10^{-20}\ \text{mol}^4\ \text{dm}^{-12} = (3x\ \text{mol dm}^{-3})^3 \times x\ \text{mol dm}^{-3}$
$\therefore\ 27x^4 = 1.25 \times 10^{-20}$
$x = (4.63 \times 10^{-22})^{1/4} = 4.64 \times 10^{-6}$
and solubility = $\mathbf{4.64 \times 10^{-6}}$ **mol dm^{-3}**

EXERCISE 47

a If [Na^+ (aq)] is increased, NaCl is precipitated in order to reduce [Na^+ (aq)] towards its original value.

b If [Cl^- (aq)] is increased, NaCl is precipitated in order to reduce [Cl^- (aq)] towards its original value.

EXPERIMENT 4

Questions

1. A colourless precipitate appeared in each tube.
2. Yes, this was predicted in Exercise 47.
3. Each ion has concentration = 5.42 mol dm^{-3}.
4. Some of the sodium ions in solution interacted with the excess chloride ions to form a precipitate of sodium chloride.
5. Some of the chloride ions in solution interacted with the excess sodium ions to form a precipitate of sodium chloride.
6. At high concentrations, ions of opposite charge interact with each other, tending to 'pair up'. This makes the effective concentration of 'free' ions very much smaller than the concentrations obtained from the amount dissolved. The equilibrium law can only be applied using concentrations if these are the same as the effective concentrations of 'free' ions, which is the case in very dilute solutions only. (Effective concentrations are known as 'activities' and, if values can be calculated, they can be used in the equilibrium law, but this is beyond A-level.)

EXERCISE 48

a

Initial concn/mol dm^{-3}		0	0.10
	$SrSO_4$ (s) ⇌	Sr^{2+} (aq) +	SO_4^{2-} (aq)
Equilibrium concn/mol dm^{-3}		x	$(0.10 + x)$

$$K_s = [Sr^{2+}\ (aq)][SO_4^{2-}\ (aq)]$$

4.0×10^{-7} mol^2 dm^{-6} = (x mol dm^{-3}) $(0.10 + x)$ mol dm^{-3}

Assume that $(0.10 + x) = 0.10$

$\therefore 4.0 \times 10^{-7} = x \times 0.10$

$\therefore x = 4.0 \times 10^{-6}$

and solubility = **4.0×10^{-6} mol dm^{-3}**

b

Initial concn/mol dm^{-3}		0	0.20
	MgF_2 (s) ⇌	Mg^{2+} (aq) +	$2F^-$ (aq)
Equilibrium concn/mol dm^{-3}		x	$(2x + 0.20)$

$$K_s = [Mg^{2+}\ (aq)][F^-\ (aq)]^2$$

7.2×10^{-9} mol^3 dm^{-9} = (x mol dm^{-3}) $(2x + 0.20)^2$ mol^2 dm^{-6}

Assume that $(2x + 0.20) \approx 0.20$

$7.2 \times 10^{-9} = x \times (0.20)^2$

$\therefore x = 1.8 \times 10^{-7}$

and solubility = **1.8×10^{-7} mol dm^{-3}**

EXERCISE 49

$K_s(SrCO_3) = 1.1 \times 10^{-10}$ mol ^{2} dm^{-6}

Since the volume is doubled

Initial concn/mol dm^{-3}			0.50
	$SrCO_3$ (s) $\rightleftharpoons$	Sr^{2+} (aq) +	CO_3^{2-} (aq)
Equilibrium concn/mol dm^{-3}		x	$(x + 0.50)$

$$K_s = [Sr^{2+}(aq)][CO_3^{2-}(aq)]$$

1.1×10^{-10} mol^2 dm^{-6} = x mol dm^{-3} × $(x + 0.50)$ mol dm^{-3}
Assume that $x \ll 0.5$ i.e. $x + 0.50 \approx 0.50$

$$\therefore\ x = \frac{1.1\times10^{-10}}{0.50} = 2.2\times10^{-10}$$

and $[Sr^{2+}(aq)]$ = **2.2×10^{-10} mol dm^{-3}**

EXERCISE 50

Before mixing, $[Ba^{2+}(aq)]$ = 0.10 mol dm^{-3}.
Mixing changes volume from 150 cm^3 to 200 cm^3.
Then $[Ba^{2+}(aq)]$ = 0.10 mol dm^{-3} × (150/200) = 0.075 mol dm^{-3}
Before mixing, $[F^-(aq)]$ = 0.050 mol dm^{-3}.
Mixing changes volume from 50 cm^3 to 200 cm^3.
Then, $[F^-(aq)]$ = 0.050 mol dm^{-3} × (50/200) = 0.0125 mol dm^{-3}
Ion product = $[Ba^{2+}(aq)][F^-(aq)]^2$
= 0.075 mol dm^{-3} × (0.0125 mol dm^{-3})^2 = 1.2×10^{-5} mol^3 dm^{-9}
Ion product is greater than K_s. Therefore **precipitation occurs.**

EXERCISE 51

a Ag^+Cl^- : 2 concentration terms, ∴ unit = (mol dm^{-3})^2 = mol^2 dm^{-6}
$Pb^{2+}2Br^-$: 3 concentration terms, ∴ unit = (mol dm^{-3})^3 = mol^3 dm^{-9}
$Ag^+BrO_3^-$: 2 concentration terms, ∴ unit = (mol dm^{-3})^2 = mol^2 dm^{-6}
$Mg^{2+}2OH^-$: 3 concentration terms, ∴ unit = (mol dm^{-3})^3= mol^3 dm^{-9}

b When equal volumes of the solution are mixed, their concentrations, before reaction, are halved: i.e. concentrations of all ions required for ion product calculations = 5.0×10^{-4} mol dm^{-3}

i) Ion product = $[Ag^+(aq)][Cl^-(aq)]$ = (5.0×10^{-4} mol dm^{-3})^2
= 2.5×10^{-7} mol^2 dm^{-6}
$> K_s$ ∴ **precipitation occurs**

ii) Ion product = $[Pb^{2+}(aq)][Br^-(aq)]^2$ = (5.0×10^{-4} mol dm^{-3})^3
= $1.25 \times 5.0 \times 10^{-10}$ mol^3 dm^{-9}
$< K_s$ ∴ **no precipitation**

iii) Ion product = $[Ag^+(aq)][BrO_3^-(aq))]$ = (5.0×10^{-4} mol dm^{-3})^2
= 2.5×10^{-7} mol^2 dm^{-6}
$< K_s$ ∴ **no precipitation**

iv) Ion product = $[Mg^{2+}(aq)][OH^-(aq)]^2$ = (5.0×10^{-4} mol dm^{-3})^3
= 1.25×10^{-10} mol^3 dm^{-9}
$> K_s$ ∴ **precipitation occurs**

EXERCISE 52

$$K_D = \frac{[\text{acid (aq)}]}{[\text{acid (ether)}]}$$

$$K_D = \frac{0.0759 \text{ mol dm}^{-3}}{0.0114 \text{ mol dm}^{-3}} = 6.66$$

$$K_D = \frac{0.108 \text{ mol dm}^{-3}}{0.0162 \text{ mol dm}^{-3}} = 6.67$$

$$K_D = \frac{0.158 \text{ mol dm}^{-3}}{0.0237 \text{ mol dm}^{-3}} = 6.67$$

$$K_D = \frac{0.300 \text{ mol dm}^{-3}}{0.0451 \text{ mol dm}^{-3}} = 6.65$$

Average K_D = **6.66**

Or, from the graph

$$\text{slope} = \frac{\Delta[\text{acid (aq)}]}{\Delta[\text{acid (ether)}]}$$

$$K_D = \frac{(0.268 - 0.050)}{(0.0400 - 0.0072)}$$

$$= \frac{0.218}{0.0328} = \mathbf{6.65}$$

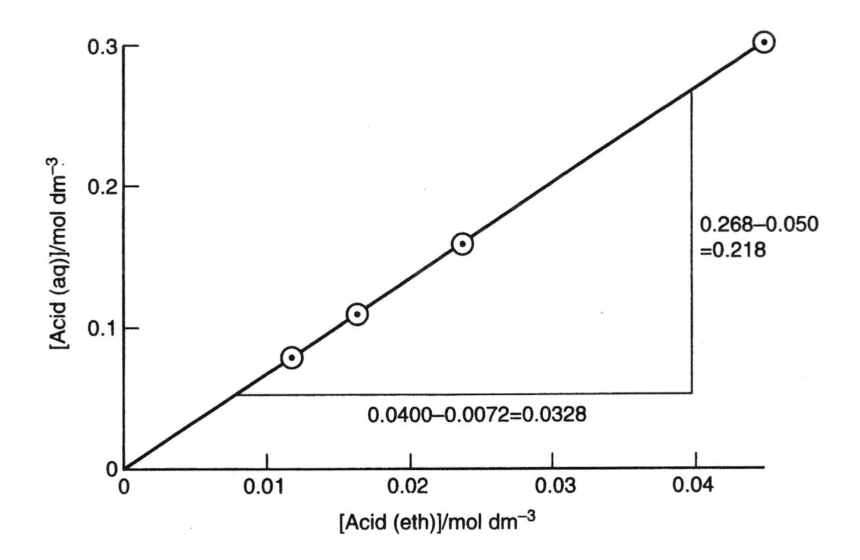

EXERCISE 53

a

Initial amount/mol	0.010	0
	NH_3 (tce) $\rightleftharpoons$	NH_3 (aq)
Equilibrium amount/mol	x	$0.010 - x$

$$K_D = \frac{[NH_3\,(aq)]}{[NH_3\,(tce)]}$$

$$290 = \frac{(0.010 - x)\ \text{mol}/0.10\ \text{dm}^3}{x\ \text{mol}/0.10\ \text{dm}^3} = \frac{(0.010 - x)}{x}$$

$$290x = 0.010 - x$$

$$x = \frac{0.010}{291} = 3.4 \times 10^{-5}$$

∴ the amount of ammonia remaining = x mol = **3.4×10^{-5} mol**

b After the first addition of water, the remaining amount of ammonia, x mol, is given by the same method as in **a**:

$$290 = \frac{(0.010 - x_1)\ \text{mol}/0.025\ \text{dm}^3}{x_1\ \text{mol}/0.10\ \text{dm}^3} = \frac{4(0.010 - x_1)}{x_1}$$

$$290x_1 = 0.040 - 4x_1$$

$$x_1 = \frac{0.040}{294} = 1.4 \times 10^{-4}$$

Note that this is $0.010 \times (4/294)$
or

$$\text{remaining amount} = \text{original amount} \times \frac{V\,(\text{tce})/V\,(\text{aq})}{K_D + V\,(\text{tce})/V(\text{aq})}$$

Thus, after the second addition

$$x_2 = \left(0.010 \times \frac{4}{294}\right) \times \frac{4}{294} = 0.010 \times \left(\frac{4}{294}\right)^2$$

and after the fourth addition

$$x_4 = 0.010 \times \left(\frac{4}{294}\right)^4 = 3.4 \times 10^{-10}$$

The amount finally remaining = x_4 mol = **3.4×10^{-10} mol**

Note that the amount remaining is reduced by a factor of 10^{-5}: clearly, the extraction is made far more efficient by dividing the extracting liquid into several portions.

EXERCISE 54

If the molecular formula in trichloromethane is $(CH_3CO_2H)_n$, then

$$K_D = \frac{[CH_3CO_2\ (aq)]^n}{[CH_3CO_2H\ (tcm)]} \quad (\text{tcm} = \text{trichloromethane})$$

Taking logarithms,

$$\log K_D = n \log [CH_3CO_2H\ (aq)] - \log [CH_3CO_2H\ (tcm)]$$

Rearranging this equation into the form $y = mx + c$

$$\log[CH_3CO_2H\ (tcm)] = n \log[CH_3CO_2H\ (aq)] - \log K_D$$

∴ a plot of log $[CH_3CO_2H\ (tcm)]$ against log $[CH_3CO_2H\ (aq)]$ should be a straight line with slope n. (Here we may use concentrations in g dm^{-3} because they are proportional to concentrations in mol dm^{-3}.)

log $([CH_3CO_2H\ (tcm)]/g\ dm^{-3})$	1.24	1.64	1.93
log $([CH_3CO_2H\ (aq)]/g\ dm^{-3})$	2.47	2.68	2.81

From the graph, the slope, $n = \frac{1.90 - 1.40}{2.80 - 2.55} = \frac{0.50}{0.25} = 2.0$

∴ the formula of ethanoic acid in trichloromethane is $\mathbf{(CH_3CO_2H)_2}$

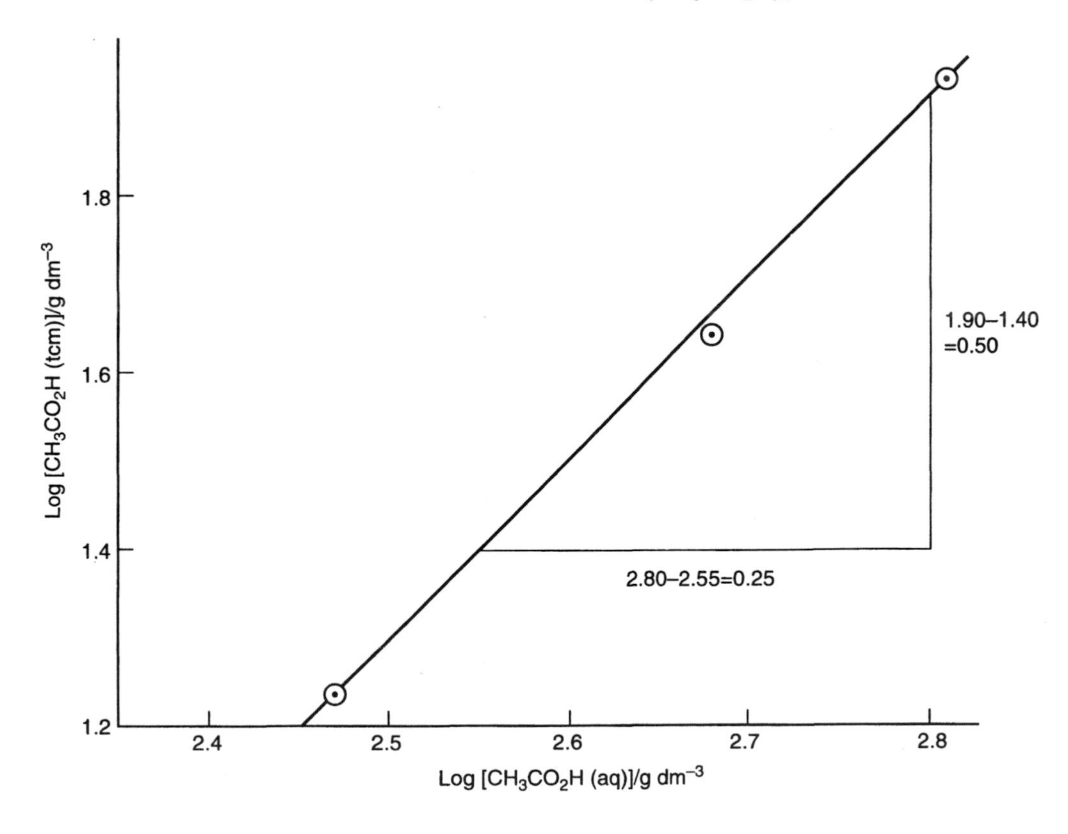

EXERCISE 55

$$K_c = \frac{[PCl_3\ (g)][Cl_2\ (g)]}{[PCl_5\ (g)]} = \frac{(1.50\times10^{-2}\ mol\ dm^{3})\times(1.50\times10^{-2}\ mol\ dm^{-3})}{1.18\times10^{-3}\ mol\ dm^{-3}}$$

$$K_c = \mathbf{0.19\ mol\ dm^{-3}}$$

EXERCISE 56

$$K_c = \frac{[SO_3\ (g)]^2}{[SO_2\ (g)]^2\ [O_2\ (g)]} = \frac{(0.92\ mol\ dm^{-3})^2}{(0.23\ mol\ dm^{-3})^2\ (1.37\ mol\ dm^{-3})} = \mathbf{11.7\ dm^3\ mol^{-1}}$$

EXERCISE 57

$$K_c = \frac{[NH_3\ (g)]^2}{[N_2\ (g)]\ [H_2\ (g)]^3} = \frac{(1.5\ mol\ dm^{-3})^2}{(13.6\ mol\ dm^{-3})\ (1.0\ mol\ dm^{-3})^3} = \mathbf{0.17\ dm^6\ mol^{-2}}$$

EXERCISE 58

$$K_c = \frac{[HI\ (g)]^2}{[H_2\ (g)]\ [I_2\ (g)]^3} \quad \therefore\ 54.1 = \frac{(3.53\times10^{-3}\ mol\ dm^{-3})^2}{(0.48\times10^{-3}\ mol\ dm^{-3}\times x)}$$

$$x = [I_2\ (g)] = \mathbf{4.8\times10^{-4}\ mol\ dm^{-3}}$$

EXERCISE 59

$$K_c = \frac{[CH_3CO_2C_5H_{11}\ (l)]}{[C_5H_{10}\ (l)]\ [CH_3CO_2H\ (l)]}$$

$$540\ dm^3\ mol^{-1} = \frac{x}{(5.66\times10^{-3}\ mol\ dm^{-3})(2.55\times10^{-3}\ mol\ dm^{-3})}$$

$$x = [CH_3CO_2C_5H_{11}\ (l)] = \mathbf{7.79\times10^{-3}\ mol\ dm^{-3}}$$

EXERCISE 60

$$K_c = \frac{[CH_3CO_2C_2H_5\ (l)]\ [H_2O\ (l)]}{[CH_3CO_2H\ (l)]\ [C_2H_5OH\ (l)]}$$

Because the same number of moles appear on both sides of the equation, it is possible to substitute amounts rather than concentrations.

$$\text{i.e. } 4.0 = \frac{0.66\ mol\times0.66\ mol}{0.33\ mol\times x}$$

$$x = \text{amount of } C_2H_5OH = \mathbf{0.33\ mol}$$

EXERCISE 61

	H_2 (g)	+ I_2 (g)	$\rightleftharpoons$ 2HI (g)
Initial amount/mol	20.57	5.22	0
Equilibrium amount/mol	15.46	0.11	10.22

Amount of H_2 at equilibrium = initial amount – amount reacted
= (20.57 – $\frac{1}{2}$ × 10.22) mol = 15.46 mol

Amount of I_2 at equilibrium = initial amount – amount reacted
= (5.22 – $\frac{1}{2}$ × 10.22) mol = 0.11 mol

$$K_c = \frac{[HI\ (g)]^2}{[H_2\ (g)]\ [I_2\ (g)]} = \frac{(10.22\ mol)^2}{(15.46\ mol)\ (0.11\ mol)} = \mathbf{61}$$

EXERCISE 62

Initial concn/mol dm^{-3}	0.1307	0
	N_2O_4 (l) $\rightleftharpoons$	$2NO_2$ (l)
Equilibrium concn/mol dm^{-3}	0.1300	0.0014

Equilibrium concentration of N_2O_4 = initial concn – concn reacted
= (0.1307 – 0.0007) mol dm^{-3} = 0.1300 mol dm^{-3}

$$K_c = \frac{[NO_2\ (l)]^2}{[N_2O_4\ (l)]} = \frac{(0.0014\ \text{mol dm}^{-3})^2}{(0.1300\ \text{mol dm}^{-3})} = \mathbf{1.51 \times 10^{-5}\ mol\ dm^{-3}}$$

EXERCISE 63

Initial amount/mol	2.0	1.0	0	0
	C_2H_5OH (l) +	CH_3CO_2H (l) $\rightleftharpoons$	$CH_3CO_2C_2H_5$ (l) +	H_2O (l)
Equilibrium amount/mol	1.155	0.155	0.845	0.845

Equilibrium amount of C_2H_5OH = initial amount – amount reacted
= (2.0 – 0.845) mol = 1.155 mol
Equilibrium amount of CH_3CO_2H = initial amount – amount reacted
= (1.0 – 0.845) mol = 0.155 mol

$$K_c = \frac{[CH_3CO_2C_2H_5\ (l)]\,[H_2O\ (l)]}{[C_2H_5OH\ (l)]\,[CH_3CO_2H\ (l)]} = \frac{(0.845\ \text{mol})(0.845\ \text{mol})}{(1.155\ \text{mol})(0.155\ \text{mol})} = \mathbf{3.99}\ \text{(volume cancels)}$$

EXERCISE 64

Initial amount/mol	8.0	6.0	0	0
	CH_3CO_2H (l) +	C_2H_5OH (l) $\rightleftharpoons$	$CH_3CO_2C_2H_5$ (l) +	H_2O (l)
Equilibrium amount/mol	8.0 – x	6.0 –x	x	x

$$K_c = \frac{[CH_3CO_2C_2H_5\ (l)]\,[H_2O\ (l)]}{[CH_3CO_2H\ (l)]\,[C_2H_5OH\ (l)]}$$

$$4.5 = \frac{x \times x}{(8.0 - x)(6.0 \times x)} = \frac{x^2}{48.0 - 14.0x + x^2}$$

$$3.5x^2 - 63.0x + 216.0 = 0$$

$$x = \frac{-(-63.0) \pm \sqrt{(-63.0)^2 - (4 \times 3.5 \times 216.0)}}{2 \times 3.5}$$

$$= \frac{63.0 \pm \sqrt{945}}{7.0} = 4.61 \text{ or } 13.4 \text{ (absurd root)}$$

$\therefore$ equilibrium amount of water = **4.6 mol**

EXERCISE 65

Initial amount/mol	0	2.0	1.0
	$2HI$ (g) $\rightleftharpoons$	H_2 (g) +	I_2 (g)
Equilibrium amount/mol	$2x$	(2.0 – x)	(1.0 –x)

$$K_c = \frac{[H_2\ (g)][I_2\ (g)]}{[HI\ (g)]^2}$$

$$0.02 = \frac{(2.0-x)(1.0-x)}{(2x)^2} = \frac{2.0-3.0x+x^2}{4x^2}$$

$$0.92x^2 - 3.0x + 2.0 = 0$$

$$x = \frac{-(-3.0) \pm \sqrt{(-3.0)^2 - (4 \times 0.92 \times 2.0)}}{2 \times 0.92} = \frac{3.0 \pm \sqrt{1.64}}{1.84}$$

$$= 0.93 \text{ or } 2.33 \text{ (absurd root)}$$

$$\text{amount of HI} = 2x = 2 \times 0.93 \text{ mol} = 1.86 \text{ mol}$$

$$[HI\ (g)] = \frac{\text{amount}}{\text{volume}} = \frac{1.86 \text{ mol}}{1.0 \text{ dm}^3} = \mathbf{1.9\ mol\ dm^{-3}}$$

$$[H_2\ (g)] = \frac{(2.0-0.93) \text{ mol}}{1.0 \text{ dm}^3} = \mathbf{1.1\ mol\ dm^{-3}}$$

$$[I_2\ (g)] = \frac{(1.0-0.93) \text{ mol}}{1.0 \text{ dm}^3} = \mathbf{0.07\ mol\ dm^{-3}}$$

EXERCISE 66

Initial amount/mol	0.019	0	0
	$PCl_5\ (g) \rightleftharpoons$	$PCl_3\ (g)\ +$	$Cl_2\ (g)$
Equilibrium amount/mol	$0.019 - x$	x	x

$$K_c = \frac{[PCl_3\ (g)]\ [Cl_2\ (g)]}{[PCl_5\ (g)]^2}$$

$$0.19 \text{ mol dm}^{-3} = \frac{(x \text{ mol}/0.75 \text{ dm}^3) \times (x \text{ mol}/0.75 \text{ dm}^3)}{(0.019-x) \text{ mol}/0.75 \text{ dm}^3}$$

$$0.19 = \frac{x^2}{(0.75)(0.019-x)}$$

$$x^2 + 0.1425x - 2.71 \times 10^{-3} = 0$$

$$x = \frac{-0.1425 \pm \sqrt{(0.1425)^2 - (4)(1)(-2.71 \times 10^{-3})}}{2 \times 1}$$

$$= \frac{-0.1425 \pm \sqrt{0.0311}}{2}$$

$$= 0.017 \text{ or } -0.159 \text{ (absurd root)}$$

$$\text{amount of } PCl_5 \text{ at equilibrium} = (0.019 - 0.017) \text{ mol} = \mathbf{2.0 \times 10^{-3}\ mol}$$

EXERCISE 67

$$K_p = \frac{p^2_{NO_2}}{p_{N_2O_4}} = \frac{(0.67 \text{ atm})^2}{0.33 \text{ atm}} = \mathbf{1.36\ atm}$$

EXERCISE 68

$$K_p = \frac{p^2_{SO_3}}{p^2_{SO_2} \times p_{O_2}} = \frac{(2.3 \text{ atm})^2}{(2.3 \text{ atm})^2 \times 4.5 \text{ atm}} = \mathbf{0.22\ atm^{-1}}$$

EXERCISE 69

$$K_p = \frac{p_{HI}^2}{p_{H_2} \times p_{I_2}} = \frac{(0.40\text{ atm})^2}{(0.25\text{ atm}) \times (0.16\text{ atm})} = \mathbf{4.0}$$

EXERCISE 70

Total amount of gas = $(6.2 \times 10^{-3} + 6.2 \times 10^{-3} + 0.994 + 0.994)$ mol
= 2.00 mol

partial pressure = mole fraction × total pressure

$$p_{CO} = \frac{6.2 \times 10^{-3}}{2.00} \times 2.0\text{ atm} = 6.2 \times 10^{-3}\text{ atm}$$

$$p_{H_2O} = \frac{6.2 \times 10^{-3}}{2.00} \times 2.0\text{ atm} = 6.2 \times 10^{-3}\text{ atm}$$

$$p_{H_2} = \frac{0.994}{2.00} \times 2.0\text{ atm} = 0.994\text{ atm}$$

$$p_{CO_2} = \frac{0.994}{2.00} \times 2.0\text{ atm} = 0.994\text{ atm}$$

$$K_p = \frac{p_{CO} \times p_{H_2O}}{p_{CO_2} \times p_{H_2}} = \frac{(6.2 \times 10^{-3}\text{ atm}) \times (6.2 \times 10^{-3}\text{ atm})}{0.994\text{ atm} \times 0.994\text{ atm}} = \mathbf{3.89 \times 10^{-5}}$$

EXERCISE 71

Total amount of gas = $(0.4 + 0.6)$ mol = 1.0 mol

$$p_I = \frac{0.40}{1.00} \times 1.0\text{ atm} = 0.40\text{ atm} \qquad p_{I_2} = \frac{0.60}{1.00} \times 1.0\text{ atm} = 0.60\text{ atm}$$

$$K_p = \frac{p_I^2}{p_{I_2}} = \frac{(0.40\text{ atm})^2}{0.60\text{ atm}} = \mathbf{0.27\text{ atm}}$$

EXERCISE 72

Total amount of gas = $(0.560 + 0.060 + 1.27)$ mol = 1.89 mol

$$p_{H_2} = \frac{0.560}{1.89} \times 2.00\text{ atm} = 0.593\text{ atm}$$

$$p_{I_2} = \frac{0.060}{1.89} \times 2.00\text{ atm} = 0.0635\text{ atm}$$

$$p_{HI} = \frac{1.27}{1.89} \times 2.00\text{ atm} = 1.34\text{ atm}$$

$$K_p = \frac{p_{HI}^2}{p_{H_2} \times p_{I_2}} = \frac{(1.34\text{ atm})^2}{0.593\text{ atm} \times 0.0635\text{ atm}} = \mathbf{47.7}$$

EXERCISE 73

Total amount of gas = (0.96 + 0.04 + 0.02) mol = 1.02 mol

$$p_{NO_2} = \frac{0.96}{1.02} \times p_T \qquad p_{NO} = \frac{0.04}{1.02} \times p_T \qquad p_{O_2} = \frac{0.02}{1.02} \times p_T$$

$$K_p = \frac{p_{NO}^2 \times p_{O_2}}{p_{NO_2}^2}$$

$$6.8 \times 10^{-6}\ \text{atm} = \frac{(0.04/1.02)^2 p_T^2 (0.02/1.02) p_T}{(0.96/1.02)^2 p_T^2}$$

$$p_T = \frac{6.8 \times 10^{-6}\ \text{atm} \times 0.886}{0.00154 \times 0.0196} = \mathbf{0.20\ atm}$$

EXERCISE 74

Total amount of gas = (2.0 + 1.0 + 4.0) mol = 7.0 mol

$$K_p = \frac{p_{CO} \times p_{H_2}}{p_{H_2O}}$$

$$3.72\ \text{atm} = \frac{\frac{2.0}{7.0} \times p_T \times \frac{1.0}{7.0} \times p_T}{\frac{4.0}{7.0} \times p_T}$$

$$p_T = \frac{3.72\ \text{atm} \times (4.0/7.0)}{(2.0/7.0) \times (1.0/7.0)} = \mathbf{52\ atm}$$

EXERCISE 75

Total amount of gas = (0.013 + 0.024) mol = 0.037 mol

$$K_p = \frac{p_{CO}^2}{p_{CO_2}}$$

$$1.9\ \text{atm} = \frac{(0.024/0.037)^2 \times p_T^2}{(0.013/0.037) \times p_T}$$

$$p_T = \frac{1.9\ \text{atm} \times (0.013/0.037)}{(0.024/0.037)^2} = \mathbf{1.6\ atm}$$

EXERCISE 76

a Total amount of gas = (1.0 + 3.6 + 13.5) mol = 18.1 mol

$$p_{NH_3} = \frac{1.0}{18.1} \times 2.0\ \text{atm} = 0.11\ \text{atm}$$

$$p_{H_2} = \frac{3.6}{18.1} \times 2.0\ \text{atm} = 0.40\ \text{atm}$$

$$p_{N_2} = \frac{13.5}{18.1} \times 2.0\ \text{atm} = 1.49\ \text{atm}$$

$$K_p = \frac{p_{NH_3}^2}{p_{H_2}^3 \times p_{N_2}} = \frac{(0.11\ \text{atm})^2}{(0.40\ \text{atm})^3 \times 1.49\ \text{atm}} = \mathbf{0.13\ atm^{-2}}$$

b

$$M_{avg} = X_{NH_3} M_{NH_3} + X_{H_2} M_{H_2} + X_{N_2} M_{N_2}$$

$$= \frac{1.0}{18.1} \times 17.0\ \text{g mol}^{-1} + \frac{3.6}{18.1} \times 2.0\ \text{g mol}^{-1} + \frac{13.5}{18.5} \times 28.0\ \text{g mol}^{-1}$$

$$= (0.94 + 0.40 + 20.9)\ \text{g mol}^{-1} = \mathbf{22.2\ g\ mol^{-1}}$$

EXERCISE 77

a Total amount of gas = (0.20 + 0.010 + 3.8) mol = 4.01 mol

$$p_{PCl_5} = \frac{0.20}{4.01} \times 3.0\text{ atm} = 0.15\text{ atm}$$

$$p_{PCl_3} = \frac{0.010}{4.01} \times 3.0\text{ atm} = 7.48 \times 10^{-3}\text{ atm}$$

$$p_{Cl_2} = \frac{3.8}{4.01} \times 3.0\text{ atm} = 2.84\text{ atm}$$

$$K_p = \frac{p_{PCl_3} \times p_{Cl_2}}{p_{PCl_5}} = \frac{7.48 \times 10^{-3}\text{ atm} \times 2.84\text{ atm}}{0.15\text{ atm}} = \mathbf{0.14\text{ atm}}$$

b

$$M_{avg} = X_{PCl_5}M_{PCl_5} + X_{PCl_3}M_{PCl_3} + X_{Cl_2}M_{Cl_2}$$

$$= \frac{0.20}{4.01} \times 208.5\text{ g mol}^{-1} + \frac{0.010}{4.01} \times 137.5\text{ g mol}^{-1} + \frac{3.8}{4.01} \times 71.0\text{ g mol}^{-1}$$

$$= (10.40 + 0.34 + 67.28)\text{ g mol}^{-1} = \mathbf{78\text{ g mol}^{-1}}$$

EXERCISE 78

a $M_{avg} = X_{NO_2}M_{NO_2} + X_{N_2O_4}M_{N_2O_4}$

$72.4\text{ g mol}^{-1} = X_{NO_2} \times 46.0\text{ g mol}^{-1} + (1 - X_{NO_2}) \times 92.0\text{ g mol}^{-1}$

$$X_{NO_2} = \frac{(92.0 - 72.4)\text{ g mol}^{-1}}{(92.0 - 46.0)\text{ g mol}^{-1}} = \frac{19.6}{46.0} = \mathbf{0.426}$$

b $p_{NO_2} = 0.426 \times 1\text{ atm} = 0.426\text{ atm}$

$p_{N_2O_4} = (1 - 0.426) \times 1\text{ atm} = 0.574\text{ atm}$

$$K_p = \frac{p^2_{NO_2}}{p_{N_2O_4}} = \frac{(0.426\text{ atm})^2}{(0.574\text{ atm})} = \mathbf{0.316\text{ atm}}$$

c

	$N_2O_4\text{ (g)}$ $\rightleftharpoons$	$2NO_2\text{ (g)}$
Initial amount/mol	1.0	0
Equilibrium amount/mol	$1 - x$	$2x$

Total amount at equilibrium = $(1 - x + 2x)$ mol = $(1 + x)$ mol

$$p_{NO_2} = \frac{\text{amount of }NO_2}{\text{total amount of gas}} \times p_T = \frac{2x}{1+x} \times 6.00\text{ atm}$$

$$p_{N_2O_4} = \frac{\text{amount of }N_2O_4}{\text{total amount of gas}} \times p_T = \frac{1-x}{1+x} \times 6.00\text{ atm}$$

$$K_p = \frac{p^2_{NO_2}}{p_{N_2O_4}}$$

$$0.316\text{ atm} = \frac{\left(\frac{2x}{1+x}\right)^2 \times (6.00\text{ atm})^2}{\left(\frac{1-x}{1+x}\right) \times 6.00\text{ atm}}$$

$$0.316 = \frac{6.00 \times 4x^2}{(1+x)(1-x)} = \frac{24.00x^2}{1-x^2}$$

$$\therefore 24.316x^2 = 0.316 \text{ and } x = \sqrt{0.0130} = 0.114$$

$$\text{mole fraction of } NO_2 = \frac{\text{amount of } NO_2}{\text{total amount}}$$

$$= \frac{2x}{1+x} = \frac{2 \times 0.114}{1.114} = \mathbf{0.205}$$

EXERCISE 79

Rearranging the expression $K_p = K_c(RT)^{\Delta n}$ and putting $\Delta n = 1$

$$K_c = \frac{K_p}{(RT)^{\Delta n}} = \frac{0.811 \text{ atm}}{0.0821 \text{ atm dm}^3 \text{ K}^{-1} \text{ mol}^{-1} \times 523 \text{ K}}$$

$$= \mathbf{1.89 \times 10^{-2} \text{ mol dm}^{-3}}$$

EXERCISE 80

$$K_p = K_c(RT)^{\Delta n} = 2.0 \text{ dm}^6 \text{ mol}^{-2} \times (0.0821 \text{ atm dm}^3 \text{ K}^{-1} \text{ mol}^{-1} \times 620 \text{ K})^{-2}$$

$$= \mathbf{7.72 \times 10^{-4} \text{ atm}^{-2}}$$

EXERCISE 81

For the equation, $\Delta n = 0$

$\therefore (RT)^{\Delta n} = 1$ and $K_p = K_c$

EXERCISE 82

a See the graph on the next page

b The slope of the graph = -3.05×10^3 K (note the minus sign)

$$\text{Since } -\frac{\Delta H^{\circ}}{2.30R} = \text{slope}$$

$$\Delta H^{\circ} = 2.30 \times 8.31 \text{ J mol}^{-1} \text{ K}^{-1} \times 3.05 \times 10^3 \text{ K} = 58\,295 \text{ J mol}^{-1}$$

$$= \mathbf{58.3 \text{ kJ mol}^{-1}}$$

c i) When $T = 375$ K, $1/T = 2.66 \times 10^{-3}$ K^{-1}
Interpolation of graph gives log K_p = **1.18**

ii) When $T = 475$ K, $1/T = 2.11 \times 10^{-3}$ K^{-1}
Interpolation of graph gives log K_p = **2.86**

iii) When $T = 550$ K, $1/T = 1.82 \times 10^{-3}$ K^{-1}
Extrapolation of graph gives log K_p = **3.74**
The assumption you made was that there is a linear relationship between log K_p and $1/T$ (i.e. ΔH° is constant).

d An increase in temperature will shift the position of equilibrium to the right resulting in the production of more NO_2. This was deduced from the graph because an increase in temperature (a decrease in the value of $1/T$) increases the value of K_p.

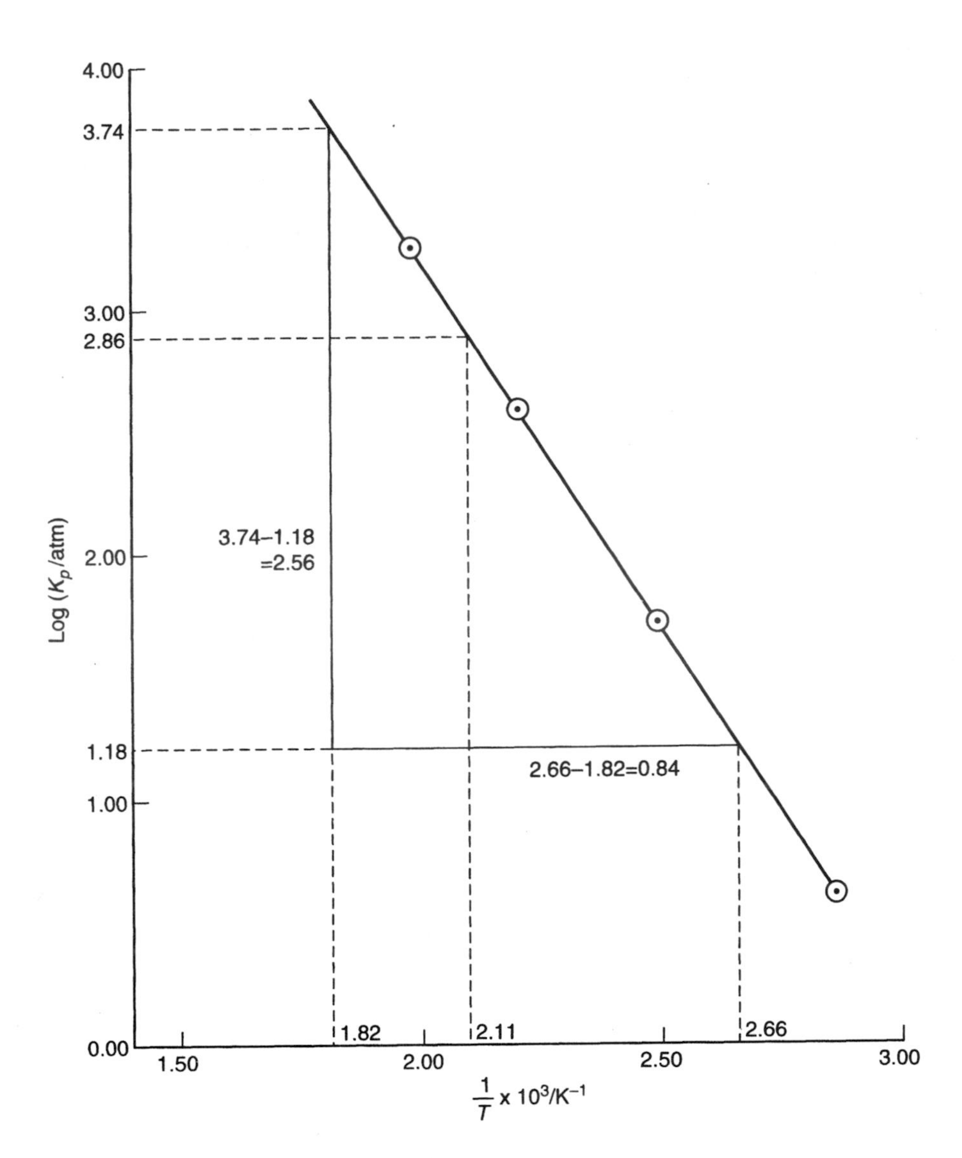

EXERCISE 83

a The slope of the graph = $+4.92 \times 10^3$ K

$$-\frac{\Delta H^{\ominus}}{2.30R} = \text{slope}$$

$$\therefore \Delta H^{\ominus} = -2.30 \times 8.31 \text{ J mol}^{-1} \text{ K}^{-1} \times 4.92 \times 10^3 \text{ K} = -94\,036 \text{ J mol}^{-1}$$
$$= \mathbf{-94.0 \text{ kJ mol}^{-1}}$$

b An increase in temperature will shift the position of equilibrium to the left, resulting in the production of more N_2 and H_2. This was deduced from the graph because an increase in temperature (a decrease in the value of $1/T$) results in a decrease in the value of K_p.

c i) The gradient for Exercise 82 is negative and the gradient for Exercise 83 is positive.

ii) The sign of $\Delta H^{\ominus}$ determines the sign of the slope. For an exothermic reaction ($\Delta H^{\ominus}$ is negative), the value of $-\Delta H^{\ominus}/2.30\ R$ is positive, giving a positive gradient. For an endothermic reaction where $\Delta H^{\ominus}$ is positive, the value of $-\Delta H^{\ominus}/2.30R$ is negative, giving a negative gradient.

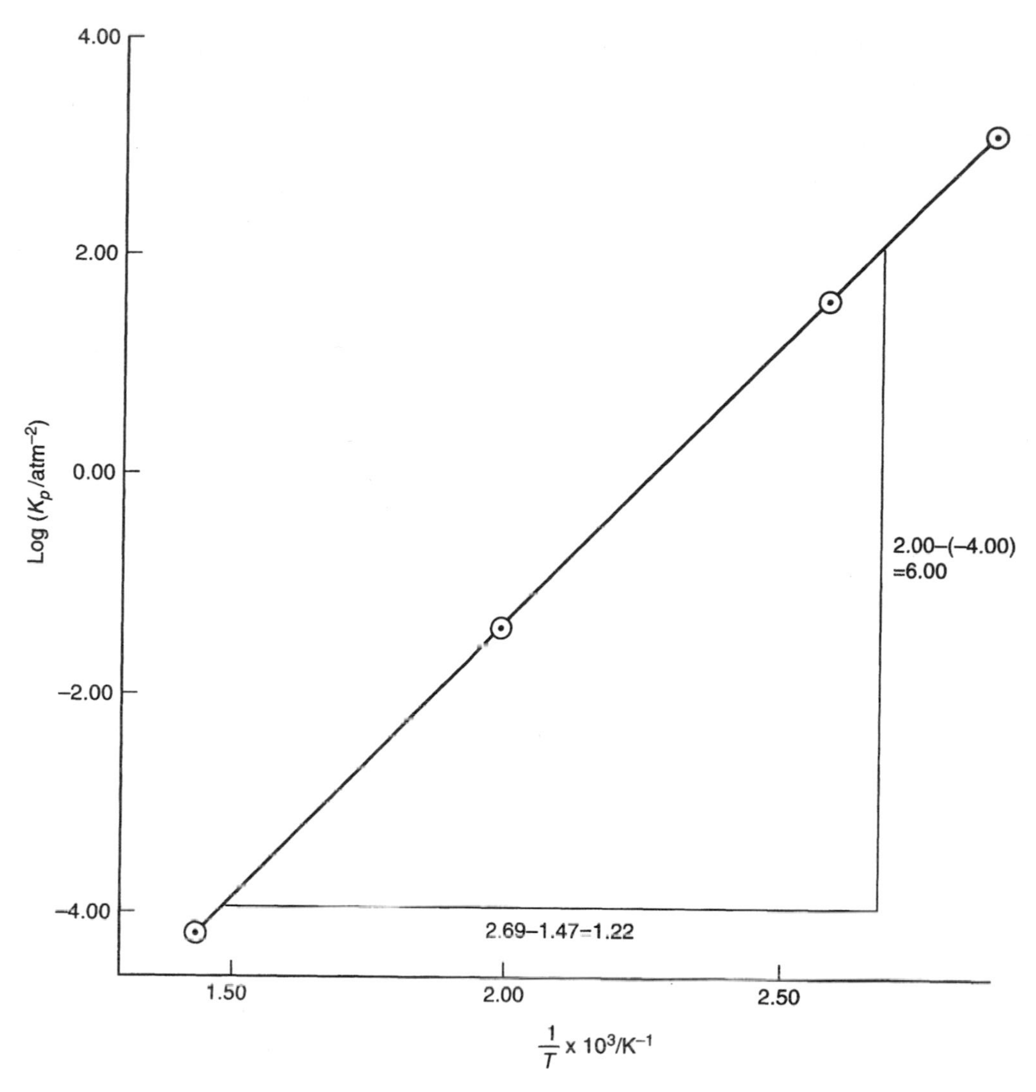

EXERCISE 84

$$\log\frac{K_2}{K_1}=\frac{\Delta H^{\circ}}{2.30R}\left(\frac{1}{T_1}-\frac{1}{T_2}\right)$$

$$\log K_2-\log 0.0118=\frac{177\,300\text{ J mol}^{-1}}{2.30\times 8.31\text{ J K}^{-1}\text{ mol}^{-1}}\left(\frac{1}{1338\text{ K}}-\frac{1}{1473\text{ K}}\right)$$

$$\log K_2=-1.928+9276.4\text{ K }(6.85\times 10^{-5}\text{ K}^{-1})=-1.293$$

$$\therefore\ K_2=\mathbf{0.0510\ atm}$$

EXERCISE 85

$$\log\frac{K_2}{K_1}=\frac{\Delta H^{\ominus}}{2.30R}\left(\frac{1}{T_1}-\frac{1}{T_2}\right)$$

$$\therefore\ \Delta H^{\ominus}=\frac{2.30R\times\log\frac{K_2}{K_1}}{\left(\frac{1}{T_1}-\frac{1}{T_2}\right)}=\frac{2.30\times 8.31\text{ J K}^{-1}\text{ mol}^{-1}\times\log\left(\frac{3.74}{2.44}\right)}{\left(\frac{1}{1000\text{ K}}-\frac{1}{1200\text{ K}}\right)}$$

$$=\frac{3.545\text{ J K}^{-1}\text{ mol}^{-1}}{1.667\times 10^{-4}\text{ K}^{-1}}=2.13\times 10^{4}\text{ J mol}^{-1}=\mathbf{21.3\ kJ\ mol^{-1}}$$

EXERCISE 86

a $K_p = \dfrac{p^2_{NO}}{p_{N_2} \times p_{O_2}}$

b From the expression for K_p above, $p^2_{NO} = K_p \times p_{N_2} \times p_{O_2}$
The values of K_p and p_{N_2} remain constant, so that $p_{NO} \propto \sqrt{p_{O_2}}$
p_{O_2} has the values 0.05 atm in the fourth column and 0.2 atm in the third.
p_{NO} is proportional to the square roots of these values.
Since $0.05 = \frac{1}{4} \times 0.2$, $\sqrt{0.05} = \frac{1}{2} \times \sqrt{0.2}$
and the value of p_{NO} in the fourth column is half that in the third.

c The table shows that the value of K_p increases with temperature. This indicates a higher yield of NO with increased temperature. Since there are the same number of molecules either side of the equation, changing the pressure will have no effect on the yield of NO.

d The reaction is endothermic, because K_p increases with temperature. Le Chatelier's principle predicts that an increase in temperature will favour an endothermic reaction.

EXERCISE 87

$$\log\frac{K_2}{K_1} = \frac{\Delta H^{\ominus}}{2.30R}\left(\frac{1}{T_1} - \frac{1}{T_2}\right)$$

Taking the values of K_p at 1800 K and 2000 K

$$\therefore \quad \Delta H^{\ominus} = \frac{2.30R \times \log\dfrac{K_2}{K_1}}{\left(\dfrac{1}{T_1} - \dfrac{1}{T_2}\right)} = \frac{2.30 \times 8.31\ \text{J K}^{-1}\ \text{mol}^{-1} \times \log\left(\dfrac{4.08}{1.21}\right)}{\left(\dfrac{1}{1800\ \text{K}} - \dfrac{1}{2000\ \text{K}}\right)}$$

$$= \frac{10.089\ \text{J K}^{-1}\ \text{mol}^{-1}}{5.56 \times 10^{-5}\ \text{K}^{-1}} = 1.81 \times 10^{5}\ \text{J mol}^{-1} = \mathbf{181\ kJ\ mol^{-1}}$$